DISCARD

THE GREAT APES

THE GREAT APES

THE NATURAL LIFE OF CHIMPANZEES,

GORILLAS, ORANGUTANS, AND GIBBONS

by Robert Gray

Illustrated with Photographs

INTRODUCTION BY GEORGE B. SCHALLER, PH.D.

W · W · NORTON & COMPANY · INC · NEW YORK

Books by Robert Gray

THE GREAT APES
CHILDREN OF THE ARK

Dedicated to Dr. Charles R. Schroeder
and the staff of The San Diego Zoo

Contents

Photographs

Introduction

No GROUP OF ANIMALS has fascinated man to the same extent as the apes, perhaps because each person sees in an ape the hairy image of himself. Unlike monkeys and other four-footed mammals, the apes look and behave like men in many ways. They sit, stretch, lie, and climb as we do. In their emotional expressions, too, they resemble us; they frown when annoyed, scratch their heads when uncertain, throw temper tantrums when frustrated. This resemblance between man and apes is hardly surprising, for both they and we evolved from some common ancestral stock. While it is true that man and ape have changed slowly over millions of years, each retains in its body and mind the evidence of this common heritage.

Man in the Western world was largely unaware of the apes until the nineteenth century, primarily because these hairy primates live in the endless tropical rain forests of Asia and Africa, areas not penetrated by explorers until recent times. A scientific distinction between chimpanzees and orangutans was not made until 1798. And only in 1847 did white men—two missionaries—discover the gorilla in West Africa. Once these manlike creatures were found, re-

ports about them were eagerly sought from travelers. Most
of these reports were mere rumors, but even the most fantastic were accepted as facts. For instance, because of the
gorilla's size and strength, and the shattering roar with which
it bullied intruders, the huge ape rapidly became a symbol
of ferocity, a manlike monster. One well-known scientist,
Richard Owen, wrote about the gorilla in 1859:

Negroes when stealing through the shades of the tropi-
cal forest, become sometimes aware of the proximity of
one of these frightfully formidable apes by the sud-
den disappearance of one of their companions, who is
hoisted into the trees, uttering, perhaps, a short chok-
ing cry. In a few minutes he falls to the ground, a
strangled corpse.

Generally, scientists and philosophers were baffled by
the ape. Some, like the French naturalist Buffon, belittled it
by calling it "nothing but a real brute . . . deprived of
thought and of every faculty which properly constitutes the
human species." Others exalted it by assigning human traits
to it, such as a ". . . sense of modesty, of honor, and of jus-
tice." The ape truly is, of course, somewhere between these
two extremes. It lacks the very complex language which is
the one truly human quality. It can grunt and scream and
hoot to indicate its emotions of the moment, but it cannot
communicate something that happened yesterday or will
happen tomorrow. The ape is marvelously intelligent, but it

has not taken that final step which separates man from the other animals.

Early in this century, as more and more apes were brought to Europe and America, scientists began to study them—their learning ability and memory. The apes' social behavior and the development of their infants were observed. Surgical operations were made on their brains, and drugs were injected into them. A great deal of knowledge rapidly accumulated about the apes, especially the chimpanzees. Whereas there were few gorillas or orangutans in captivity, chimpanzees flourished. They became favorite laboratory animals because of their willingness to solve puzzles and other problems.

However, an ape in captivity is no more a natural, typical ape than a man in prison is a typical man. It may be contented, but it cannot wander where it pleases, search for its own food, or choose its companions. Virtually nothing was known about the life of apes in the wild until recently. Brief studies were attempted in the jungle some thirty years ago, but little was learned about any of them except for one, the gibbon. However, in the past ten years, thorough studies, each lasting a year or more, have been made on the four kinds of apes. Now we know the gorilla as a good-natured vegetarian (eater of vegetation), not an aggressive beast; the orangutan is a shy and solitary figure of the treetops, not a kidnaper of women as was once claimed. A true picture now exists of the life of the apes in their forest home, a picture far more fascinating than the fables. Chimpanzees, for instance, may use leaves to clean their bottoms, and they thump the buttress roots of trees like drums. But in spite of all that is known about apes, much still needs to be added. Some, like the pygmy chimpanzee and several species of gibbon, have never been studied, and even for the other apes our knowledge is incomplete.

Mr. Gray has used recent scientific reports about apes as the basis for an accurate and delightful account of their habits. He has also noted rightly that just when man is beginning to understand the apes, he is on the verge of exterminating them. Only about five thousand orangutans and somewhere around ten thousand mountain gorillas survive in the world—not enough to fill all the seats in a sports stadium. Now that man has conquered the earth and its creatures, it is only ethical that he provide the last of his relatives with space where they can live in peace and security.

George B. Schaller, Ph.D.
Arusha, Tanzania
December, 1968

THE GREAT APES

Proconsul. This is an artist's conception drawn from fossils.

CHAPTER 1

Of Apes and Men

Once upon a time....

About ten million years ago, long before man appeared on earth, a small, monkeylike creature, whom we call Proconsul, scurried through the forests of Africa. He was about the size of a chimpanzee and had a round head, a slender body, long arms and legs, and well-developed feet and hands. He was probably covered with hair. Unlike his monkey ancestors, he had no tail, and also, quite unmonkeylike, he spent much of his time out of the trees.

He must have been very timid on the ground. For millions of years his ancestors had been tree dwellers, and during that time their bodies had changed to adapt to tree life. Proconsul had inherited these changes. While they were beneficial for a creature who spent his time among the branches, they did very little to prepare him for the dangers of life on the ground. So when Proconsul dropped from the trees, he had no claws or fangs with which to defend himself; neither could he run so fast as the predators who hunted him; and certainly, he was not so strong as they. Consequently, he stayed close to the trees, and at the first sign of danger scampered back aloft. He remained very much a creature of the forest.

Pronconsul and creatures very much like him were among nature's most important evolutionary experiments. They were members of a group of monkeylike apes (or apelike monkeys) with the tongue-twisting name *Dryopithecus* (pronounced DRY-OH-PITH-IH-CUSS). These animals first appeared in Africa, and for the fifteen million years or so of their existence they expanded their range until it covered southern Europe and Asia. They included several species and sizes. Some were as small as chimpanzees, and others—the giants of the group—were as large as gorillas. They were important evolutionary experiments because from these Dryopithecines, Proconsul among them, probably came today's great apes and even man himself.

But we are not sure. Trying to trace an animal back to its beginnings is like working a jigsaw puzzle in which most of the pieces are missing. Although we can put together the overall picture, without these missing pieces we must guess at many of the details. And this is the problem we face in trying to solve the puzzle of evolution. Here, our pieces are the fossilized remains we find—maybe a few teeth, or a bone. Perhaps we find a whole skull in some prehistoric tar pit, or uncover a complete skeleton in a stone quarry or mine.

But more often than not, the scientists, called paleontologists, who work on the puzzle of evolution must rely on mere bits and scraps for their information.

One of the most difficult problems they must contend with is the matter of time. The paleontologist must search back into time—often millions of years—for the pieces that make up his puzzle. And the further back he looks, the fewer pieces he finds. Most disappeared long ago. They were buried by earthquakes, dissolved by the sea, or eaten by other animals. Evolution is an extremely slow process, and to the paleontologist, the millions of years involved are like attics in which the pieces of his puzzle are hidden. And he realizes that, all too often, junk gets hopelessly mixed up with the few treasures one finds in attics.

But what does the term "millions of years" really mean? It is very difficult to conceive of such expanses of time. Maybe it would help if we were to invent a game in which time becomes distance—inches, feet and miles. Suppose that one year, the time between one birthday and the next, is one inch long. That is, one year stands there in front of you, one inch from your nose. A century—one hundred years—is one hundred inches, or about eight feet away, maybe hanging on the wall across the room. One thousand years—about one-half of the Christian era—is roughly eighty-three feet from where you are sitting, out of the

house and down the street. But that is just the beginning
in our measure of time. One million years, not a very long
time in the paleontologist's work, is ten miles away, probably well outside of your town.

Proconsul lived about ten million years ago, a distance of one hundred miles away from you in our game.
And in order to find him and trace his evolution, science
has searched each of those miles—or years—inch by inch.

From what we *have* found, a picture has begun to
emerge in our puzzle. Although we must guess about some
of the empty spots, we know enough to be sure that our
guesses are fairly accurate. Life appeared on earth, possibly
more than two billion years ago (roughly two hundred
thousand miles—about the distance from the earth to the
moon in our game). Animals began in the sea as simple,
one-celled creatures, then slowly developed into species that
swam or crawled on the bottom. Millions of years later,
they struggled onto the land as primitive amphibians to
live in the swamps, then slowly moved out to inhabit the
forests, the grasslands, and the air. During all these years
they changed, very slowly to be sure, but steadily, from
simple forms into extremely complicated creatures. Fish
changed to become better swimmers; birds, better fliers;
mammals, more able hunters, runners or climbers, and so
on. Often, there were evolutionary mistakes. Thousands of
species appeared, only to die away because they could not
adapt to a changing earth or compete with other species.

This, for instance, is what happened to the dinosaurs. After ruling the world for a hundred and fifty million years, the dim-witted beasts could not keep pace with the changing earth. They were designed for warm, moist climates, and as the earth became cooler, the dinosaurs died, to be replaced by a new animal—the mammal. Since it first appeared about seventy million years ago, this hairy little creature has played an increasingly important role in the story of life. We humans might like to say *the most* important role," for, after all, we are mammals and like to think of ourselves as the finest products of evolution.

Of course, Proconsul was also a mammal and had the traits which all mammals share. First, he was warm-blooded, that is, his body temperature stayed the same regardless of the temperature of the surrounding air. Next, he had hair on his body instead of scales or feathers. And his babies were born alive instead of in eggs; after being born, they nursed on their mothers' milk. Today, mammals are more widespread on earth than any other creature except insects, and the group includes such different animals as the one-hundred-and-fifty-ton blue whale and the tiny dwarf shrew, which weighs a mere one-quarter ounce, about as much as a dime.

Mammals seemed to represent nature's finest experiment, but evolution did not stop when they appeared on earth. Far from it. One of the basic demands of life is that a new form continue to grow and evolve. So, unlike the dinosaurs, the mammals, with their marvelously adaptable bodies, steadily developed into forms that would fit into earth's many changing environments. These environments, called "ecological niches," include different climates—such as hot or cold, dry or wet; different foods—meat or grass, fruit or insects; and various types of homelands—sandy, rocky, grassland, forest, sea, or lake. Some mammals, such as moles, became true earth dwellers, living in tunnels which they bored through the soil. Others, such as deer, cattle, horses, and so on, became grass eaters. The carnivores, or meat eaters, preyed on these grazing herds. One mammal, the bat, took to the air and is the only true flier in the mammal group. Some mammals, perhaps finding life on land too strenuous, slipped back into the sea to become the whales and seals that we have today. And one mammal climbed into the trees. We call him a primate. This group includes the shrews, marmosets, lemurs, monkeys, apes, and man.

There are about two hundred species of living primates. The most primitive is the tree shrew; the most complex is man. Within such a wide range of creatures, you might expect difficulty in defining the word "primate," for, after all, a man and a shrew seem to have little in common. They share the mammalian qualities—hair, live birth and nursing of the young—but what else do they share? There is a certain similar pattern in primate brains, there are similarities in the fingers and toes, and there are other like-

Tree shrew (Tupaia glis). *This squirrel-sized primitive primate lives in southeastern Asia.*

nesses. But no group of primates, whether tree shrew, marmoset, lemur, monkey, ape, or man, has all of these features.

There *is* one ability that most share, but even here we must be careful, for the tree shrew lacks it. However, it is general enough among primates to be called a common trait. This is the ability to climb by grasping. Primates are essentially tree dwellers and, among them, only man has given up this heritage. The others spend all or part of their lives off the ground. About sixty million years ago, the first primates appeared in trees and their descendants developed and prospered there. Because evolution favors those species which adapt best to their environments, the primates changed over the ages. They developed long fingers and toes that ended in flat nails instead of claws, so they did not have to dig into a tree's bark in order to climb. With this grasping ability they could hold on by a hand or foot while they reached out for food. They could scamper rapidly away from their ancient enemy, the leopard, who climbed by digging his claws into the tree. And to become even better tree dwellers, some primates developed the ability to swing along, hand over hand, under a branch, a process called brachiating. The present-day gibbon is the most capable of all brachiators.

During the millions of years of their development in trees, the primates changed in other ways. Their eyes moved from the sides of their heads to the front of their

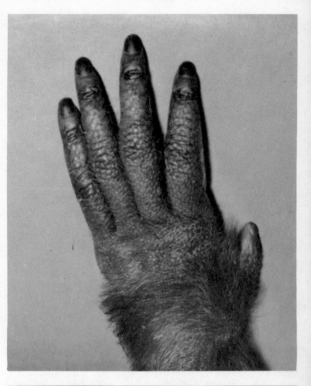

Hand of an orangutan. Early in their evolution, primates developed long, broad hands with fingers and nails.

Leopard (Panthera pardus). *Like most mammals, it has paws and claws.*

Zebra (Equus burchelli). *He has poor depth vision because of his long nose and the placement of his eyes on the sides of his head.*

faces. This seemingly simple adjustment gave them the ability to judge distance. It is this ability, called binocular, or depth, vision, that allows a monkey to know exactly how far to jump and, in humans, helps a woman thread a needle, or a driver judge the distance of the car ahead. Because primates lived in trees, they had little use for the powerful limbs of ground-dwelling animals, but they did need to be agile and quick. So they developed long, slender arms and legs to help in swinging and climbing. Their brains, among

Chimpanzee (Pan troglodytes). *Like all higher primates, including man, the chimpanzee's eyes are on the front of his face, giving him excellent depth vision.*

the best in the animal world, developed to give them quick responses to the world of trees.

How long has this process of primate development been going on? The first primate that we know about was a shrew-like animal called a prosimian, meaning "before the ape," who lived sixty million years ago. He was about the size of a mouse and, in fact, looked like one. After spreading over much of the earth, he was replaced as king among the primates by the more intelligent monkeys. But he didn't completely disappear, and prosimians still exist in South America, Africa, and Asia. Their last remaining stronghold is the island of Madagascar off eastern Africa, where, for whatever reason, monkeys did not develop. Madagascar's prosimians are called lemurs and range from tiny, mouse-sized creatures to rugged animals that grow to be the size of large dogs. They differ widely in appearance and behavior. Some look like foxes, others like squirrels. Some have large round eyes and prowl the forests at night. Others love the sun and stretch out in the trees to warm themselves. Some eat only plant life; others raid birds' nests or hunt small animals. Madagascar is a living museum of the time, sixty million years ago, when prosimians were the highest form of primate.

Elsewhere in the world, the monkeys took over the trees. They were lightweight (a vital requirement for true tree life), agile, and smart. In the western hemisphere, many species developed a prehensile tail for grasping, and they

Ring-tailed lemurs (Lemur catta).

used it much as an elephant uses his trunk. We don't know why African and Asian monkeys did not develop this feature.

Then, about twenty-five million years ago a new primate, our old friend Proconsul, appeared in Africa. So far as we know, he was the first primate successfully to make the hazardous trip from life in the trees to life on the ground.

And it was hazardous. Tree life was safe. Very few carnivores could catch those primates who stayed off the ground. Occasionally, a leopard, python, or eagle might carry off a victim, but for the primates who stayed healthy and active, life in the trees was safer than in any other place on earth. So Proconsul's short journey to the ground was filled with danger, and he probably made sure that he could scamper back up to safety.

Why in the world would he choose to leave the trees? He was safe there and had plenty of food—fruit, leaves, buds, birds' eggs. With his marvelous hands, feet, and eyes he was beautifully adapted to life in the trees. His ancestors had lived among them for milllions of years. The trees were home. Why leave?

To find the answer, we must look at the phenomenon called "adaptive radiation," a term used by scientists to describe the evolution of life into new environments—new ecological niches. The primates, for example, had developed over millions of years to the point where they had met all the challenges that tree life presented. They could probably experience little further development without a drastic change in their lives. They had to leave the trees. So those who were the smartest or bravest or most aggressive dropped to the ground. They radiated from their ecological niche to a new one.

The Dryopithecines, including Proconsul, seem to have been the ones who made the jump. Some of them adjusted—adapted—to the shock of leaving home (maybe it took a million years or so) and fared quite well. We can say that their adaptive radiation was to fill the niche of life on the ground, and in this niche they continued to develop.

But we must not suppose that those primates who stayed behind in the forest did not continue to develop. One of the basic laws of life is that a species must continue to grow—change—or die. There are always new problems to meet—temperature and humidity changes, different food sources, and new predators, to name a few—and life must adapt to them. But perhaps the rate of change among those who stayed in the trees was much slower than among the others. We have studied these forest dwellers—the gorillas, chimpanzees, orangutans, and gibbons—for only a few hundred years, so we have not had time to see the changes that are taking place within them. However, over the past couple of million years they have not evolved so dramatically as have the Dryopithecines, which went on to become man.

A long, long trail....

Just as in any family, the members of the Dryopithecine family were not exactly alike; some were larger than

others, or more agile, or smarter. But since they were so
closely related, they had much in common. First, they were
primates, with hands and feet instead of claws or hooves.
They had forward-looking eyes and the depth vision these
provided. Their brains were the most advanced of any in
the animal kingdom. The Dryopithecines had developed
beyond the monkeys, who were still trapped in a life
among the branches. Although not truly bipedal—that is,
two-legged—the Dryopithecines probably moved in a
slouched position, and were evolving toward an upright
stance. Monkeys stayed true quadrupeds—four-legged
animals—and, in common with other quadrupeds, they
swung their legs back and forth, parallel with their bodies.
The Dryopithecines could swing their legs and arms outward as well, an ability that the apes and men share today
and which makes these limbs more usable. As Proconsul
and his Dryopithecine relatives developed toward a two-
legged posture, they changed in other ways. They lost the
narrow chest of the monkeys and developed broader, flatter
upper torsos. Their legs became stronger in order to support
them on the ground. And, of course, they lost their tail, a
feature which still distinguishes apes from most monkeys,
the tailless Barbary "apes" being a notable exception.

But the physical differences between the species that
made up the Dryopithecine family, minor as they might
appear to be, proved very important. Because of them and
the slightly different living habits they produced, the family gradually split up. Each species took off on its own

evolutionary trail. Some, the misfits, took paths that led to dead ends. These species became extinct. But others went on to develop into the primates we know today. Some stayed among the trees and became the apes—the African chimpanzees and gorillas and the orangutans of Asia. (The other Asian apes, the gibbons, left the family much earlier.) Finally, at least one of the Dryopithecines, maybe Proconsul, moved down the evolutionary path that led to man.

Those who became extinct need not concern us here. They joined the thousands of other species who had missed the mark. Because they didn't adapt or compete so well as other species, they wore out their evolutionary welcome. Our jigsaw puzzle of evolution has thousands of these rejected pieces.

What happened to the ones who were successful?

The Dryopithecine who took the path that led toward man chose a most adventurous route. First, he had to leave the trees forever. The others, those that became apes, stayed in the forests, and that is where we find them today. But man's ancestor moved onto the grasslands, a terribly hazardous place for such a defenseless creature. However, what he lacked in strength, speed, or built-in weapons he made up in intelligence. His millions of years in the trees had given him a fine brain capable of quick responses to changing conditions. One of this brain's first problems in the new life was to solve the matter of providing food and protection for its owner.

Proconsul, or whoever the creature was, had a pair of

magnificent hands, not claws, but hands. However, so long as he went around on four legs, these hands were used simply as feet. If they could be freed of this function, they could feed and protect him. He must stand erect. And that is exactly what he did. Not overnight of course. It took a few million years for Proconsul to straighten up. But the important fact is that he did. Then his hands were free to carry a club for defense, or throw a rock to bring down game animals. His eyes, which had been so important in judging the distance from one branch to another during life in the trees, were equally capable of judging where to swing the club or throw the rock. And the brain, which had kept the species nimble-witted and alert in the swaying, wind-blown world of the treetops, eventually went on to give the new two-legged primate the highest reasoning ability of all animals.

During the millions of years that this descendant of the old Dryopithecine family was working his way along the evolutionary path that led to man, the other relatives had been busy at their own development. For whatever reason, they stayed in the forest, some spending all their time aloft, others living on the ground near the trees. Much of the earth was covered by tropical forests in those days, so the forefathers of the great apes, being forest animals, were free to wander widely. We have found their remains, not only in Africa where they first developed, but in Europe and Asia as well. The Asian Dryopithecines became today's orangutans. The European members of the family died out, unable to adapt when a slight cooling of the earth's climate killed the tropical forests which grew that far north. But the African Dryopithecines flourished, and over tens of thousands of years two distinct lines of development appeared. One went on to become chimpanzees, the other, gorillas.

As the members of the Dryopithecine family evolved toward apedom, what changes appeared? In those who remained true tree dwellers, the arms became longer and the legs shorter than among the apes who spent part or all of their time on the ground. At the other extreme, the ground-dwelling apes developed into huge animals who were far too big to be tree creatures.

The hands and feet of the new apes changed to reflect their ways of living. Among the trees dwellers, the great toe moved back on the foot to let the foot act as another grasping tool. But on the gorilla, a ground dweller, the great toe moved into line with the others to help support his immense weight. Gibbons and the orangutans spend almost all of their time aloft, so their hands became hooklike, ideal for hanging from a branch.

And among all the apes, and in man also, one of nature's truly remarkable developments occurred: the opposable thumb.

Look carefully at your hand. It is flat and broad, with four fingers which grow in a line at the forward end, and a thumb which sprouts from well back on the palm. If

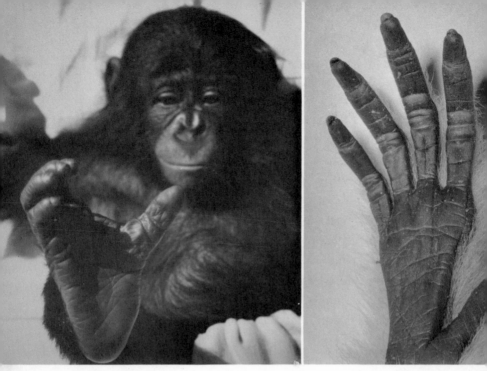

RICHARD PALMER
SAN DIEGO ZOO

Left: Lynette the pygmy chimpanzee (Pan paniscus). This diapered zoo baby, a creature of the trees, has feet designed for grasping. Her great toe is well back on her foot and acts as a thumb.

Right: Hand of a gibbon. It is long, thin, and hooklike, designed to allow the gibbon to hang from branches.

RICHARD PALMER

Amy, like all humans, has feet that are designed to support her when she stands erect. Her great toe is in line with the others.

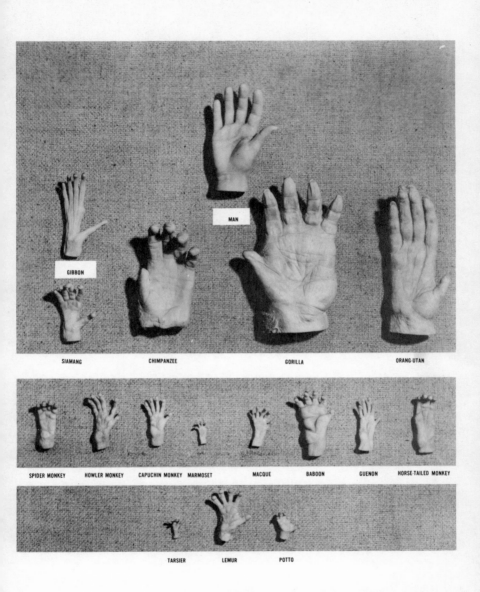

MAN

GIBBON

SIAMANG   CHIMPANZEE   GORILLA   ORANG-UTAN

SPIDER MONKEY   HOWLER MONKEY   CAPUCHIN MONKEY   MARMOSET   MACQUE   BABOON   GUENON   HORSE-TAILED MONKEY

TARSIER   LEMUR   POTTO

Hands of primates, including man and the great apes.

Adult male gorilla (Gorilla g. gorilla). *Gorillas and the other higher primates can use their opposable thumbs to handle objects.*

you stretch your thumb outward, you can see that it actually grows at almost a right angle to the palm. Now, slowly
bend your thumb until it touches the tip of each of your
fingers. This is what is meant by an opposable thumb; it can
touch each of the fingertips.

Why is it so important? A simple experiment will
demonstrate. Holding your thumb tightly against the edge
of your hand, try to pick up a pencil using only your fingers.
Now pick up the pencil in the usual way, by using your
thumb and fingers. Is there any question which was the
easier? With this opposable thumb, nature gave you a pair
of pincers. It can pick up food, hold a pencil, or turn the
pages of this book. We use it in countless ways. Although we

RICHARD PALMER

*Like Dorothy, humans have the most highly developed opposable
thumbs of all primates.*

humans share this ability with the apes, we have developed it to a much higher degree than they have. We don't know exactly why. A good guess would be that as man's brain continued to develop, it sent increasingly more complex orders to his hand, thus forcing the thumb to become a more efficient tool. The apes in their life among the trees didn't need a thumb which was so highly developed.

But the point at which man forever parted company with the apes was when his ancestors finally stood erect. In shifting the balance of his body from horizontal to vertical, man forced changes within his body which the apes would

SAN DIEGO ZOO

Standing chimpanzee. Like all apes, he cannot straighten his knees.

never experience. His spine changed its shape from the slight arch of a four-legged animal to the "S"-shaped curve we have today. His legs grew longer and stronger because he was putting all of his weight on them. He developed the ability to straighten his knees—to lock them—so that his weight passed in a straight line of bone from his hips to the ground. An ape cannot straighten his knees, so he must stand crouched—a very tiring position. Man developed a powerful rump muscle, called the *gluteus maximus*, that pulled his body forward over his legs as he walked upright. An ape, not having this muscle so highly developed, shuffles

RICHARD PALMER

Ann. Humans can lock their knees in a straight position when they stand erect.

along when trying to walk on two legs. Man's head tipped forward on his spine when he stood up, bringing his eyes into a position from which they could look forward easily. In order to make room for his brain, his head grew rounder and higher.

And, of course, man's brain, which would move him far from Proconsul and the rest of the Dryopithecine family, continued to develop. It made him a tool using creature. It gave him the power of speech, the ability to read and write, the capacity to remember clearly and for a long time. Today, man can learn and can remember what he has learned. He has become an inventor. He raises cities, builds dams, probes into space, and frees the atom.

Indeed, there are many differences between man and the apes. But at the same time, the two are very much alike. The great apes, for instance, resemble man more closely than they do the monkeys. They have a rightful claim to being our closest relatives—evolutionary cousins.

Today, some ten million years or so after Proconsul scurried among the trees, five of his descendants are living. One is man. The others are what we call the great, or anthropoid (meaning "manlike") apes—the chimpanzee, gorilla, orangutan, and—since he came from the same stock, although at an earlier date—the gibbon. We have studied our favorite subject, man, for hundreds of years and written millions of words about him. The apes are not nearly so well recorded, and only recently have we begun to study them seriously. For many thousands of years we didn't even know they existed. And even after finding them, it took us a long time to recognize and acknowledge them as the relatives who travelled along with us on those dim paths leading from Dryopithecus. It has been a long time since we were one family living together in the forest. We have all changed. In the following pages we will visit those members of the family who stayed in the old home, and will learn how life is for them. Here are four stories about our cousins —Toto the chimpanzee, Kinguti the gorilla, Pongo the orangutan, and Lar the gibbon.

Two-year-old chimpanzee.

CHAPTER 2

Toto

Toto the chimpanzee awoke at dawn, cold and hungry.
Beside him in the nest, his mother was still sleeping, curled
on her side with her legs drawn up against her body. Toto
squirmed closer to her. He snuggled deep into the warmth
of her hair, found her breast, and began nursing. In a few
moments, he was asleep again.

Around the nest, the rain forest of western Uganda
stood quietly in the early morning light, its topmost layer, or
canopy, silhouetted like a sea of black umbrellas against the
eastern skyline. Giant mahogany trees, some of them one
hundred and fifty feet tall, made up the canopy. In a matter
of minutes the light moved rapidly across their crowns, slid
down the trunks to the next level of branches, and was lost
as it passed through the leaves, branches, and vines still
lower in the forest. Only the brightest sunlight could pene-
trate to the ferns and bushes that grew on the ground,

and then only where a fallen tree had opened the canopy to the sky.

In those last few moments of dawn, the forest lay still, with only the falling of the night's dew breaking the silence. Later in the day there would be animal noises—chirps, screams, yells, whoops, buzzes, flaps, and a thousand others. But as yet, none of the forest creatures was awake.

The nocturnal, or nighttime, animals had settled into their day's sleep. Komba the galago, or bush baby, his belly filled with birds' eggs and insects, lay curled with two other bush babies in the fork of a barkcloth tree. Vava the bat hung head downward in a hollow log after his nightlong flight through the forest, when he had swept up hundreds of insects. Mhelele the tree hyrax slept in a dense clutter of undergrowth. Nende the blue duiker antelope, only thirteen inches tall at his shoulders, lay in a thicket.

The night was over.

But the day had not yet truly arrived, and the diurnal animals, those that were awake during the daylight hours, still slept away the last few minutes of the disappearing night. Tembo the elephant dozed with his herd among the grasses that grew in the valley swampland. Nyati the buffalo lay among the dense undergrowth at the forest's edge. Chui the leopard slept stretched out on a heavy branch twenty feet off the ground. And the birds were sleeping—the hornbills and guinea fowl, the francolins and starlings, woodpeckers, cuckoos, parrots, touracos, rol-

lers, and a dozen other species. The cold-blooded animals—
the lizards, snakes, and daytime insects—lay inactive,
chilled by the night's coolness.

As the sky grew brighter, colors emerged from the forest's blackness—the dark, moist greenery of leaves; brownish
blacks of wet twigs and small branches; the reddish browns
of the trees' scaffolding. The pearl-gray light warmed to
pink along the eastern skyline. Then, the sun popped above
the horizon and the light exploded in a burst of reds and
oranges across the sky.

The forest's animals came rapidly awake. Birds stood
on the edges of nests or on branches, fluffing the night's
dew from their wings. Feathers were groomed, heads
scratched, and then it was time to swoop into the day's bus-
iness. Chirps, trills, caws, squawks, a thousand different
songs were sung, each announcing that the owner of this
branch or that treetop was awake and ready to defend his
territory. Insects were caught as they lay on branches or flew
upward toward the sunlight. A casqued hornbill flapped
heavily from one tree to another for no apparent reason,
then lumbered back to where he had started. A flash of scarlet
wing feathers announced a touraco flitting among the trees.
A flock of noisy gray-bodied parrots darted among the treetops, their red tail feathers seeming to blaze in the sunlight.

Other animals awakened. In his swamp, Tembo the
elephant reached out with his trunk and stripped away an
enormous mouthful of leaves from a nearby tree. Nyati the

buffalo left his bedding spot at the forest's edge and moved back into the shadows among the trees, where he could spend the day browsing on tender shoots and leaves. Chui the leopard awoke, jumped down from her tree, and padded away, searching for food. The buzzing of insects rose to a hum that would not subside until the evening. A python, warmed by the morning sun, uncoiled its eleven-foot-long body and slipped noiselessly into the forest. A bateleur eagle dived from the sky, its claws flexed to seize the gecko it had spotted on a tree trunk. But the bird was young and inexperienced. It missed the lizard's body, and its headlong plunge was rewarded by only the tail. The gecko, tailless but still alive, scurried farther up the tree trunk. And in a nest higher in the same tree, Toto the chimpanzee awoke for the second time that day.

He squirmed uncomfortably in the nest, a crude platform of twigs and leaves which his mother had built high in a mahogany tree. He tried to nuzzle closer to his mother to nurse again, but she pushed him aside, for he was two years old and well on the way to being weaned. Toto squealed in annoyance at her rejection, but she continued pushing and he had little choice but to climb out of the nest and sit on its edge.

He was a pink-faced, large-eared youngster with bright, mischievous eyes, a round head, and a black, furry body. He had a rump patch—a tuft of snow-white hair growing on his bottom—which would gradually fade away as he grew. Because he was still a baby, he had a flat face and round forehead, unlike adult chimpanzees who have protruding snouts and sloping foreheads. When standing, he was three feet tall, and he weighed about twenty-five pounds, as much as an average-sized dog. When he matured six or seven years later, he would weigh almost one hundred and sixty pounds and stand five feet tall. And as with all the great apes, his normal lifespan would be between twenty-five and thirty years.

Toto was annoyed. For most of his two years, when he was hungry he had crawled or run to his mother and she had scooped him up and let him nurse. But for the past six months, things had been different. Not only was he at the weaning age, but another baby had taken his place at his mother's breast. Even as he sat on the edge of the nest, whimpering and acting like a spoiled child, his mother clambered to his side, holding a three-month-old infant, Toto's new sister. The baby clung to the mother's hair, an instinct with which it had been born and which saved it from a tumble to the ground below. The little chimpanzee appeared to be all legs and arms as it buried its head against its mother's breast. Its ears and eyes seemed too large for its tiny round head, and its hair, unlike the rich, black coat worn by Toto and his mother, was fine and thin, exposing the pinkish-gray skin beneath it.

The baby was nursing; Toto reached out to pull her away. His mother cuffed him on the side of the head. Then,

as though to say that she still loved him, she groomed his back as they sat on the edge of the nest. Despite the myths that humans have invented about apes' grooming habits, Toto's mother was not looking for fleas. Neither she, Toto, nor the new baby had any. In order for any animal, including man, to have fleas, that animal must live in the same nest or burrow or house for at least several weeks, long enough for the fleas' eggs to hatch. Wild chimpanzees change their sleeping place each night; consequently they are flealess. But the mother chimpanzee did find flakes of dried skin, seeds, and a few lice. She carefully parted the hairs and searched along Toto's back with her eyes just inches away. When she found something, she gently picked it out of the hair and popped it into her mouth. Grooming either herself or another chimpanzee was her main daily social activity.

Around her, other chimpanzees were climbing out of their nests, yawning and scratching themselves with long sweeps of their arms. Toto, his mother and the baby were part of an average-sized group of eleven chimpanzees, most of them females with at least one infant or older youngster. Two or three childless females and immature males were also part of the group. As they climbed from their nests which hung in half-a-dozen nearby trees, the chimpanzees called back and forth to each other—grunts, low-pitched barks, and the whimpering of babies. The older youngsters, those between four and six years old, had built nests of their own and now swung down from them, ready to start the

SAN DIEGO ZOO

Infant chimpanzee.

Chimpanzees spend much of their time grooming themselves and others.

day. Toto climbed down to the ground alone but waited there for his mother, for he stayed close to her and would continue to do so for another three or four years.

She dropped from the tree and without so much as a backward glance moved off to find food. Toto screamed at being left behind, galloped after her, and pulled himself onto her back, where he rode along like a jockey. His baby sister clung underneath.

The chimpanzees would spend six to eight hours of their day foraging and filling their stomachs. They nibbled on leaves and buds as they moved along the trails worn into the forest floor. Toto reached out from his mother's back and broke a stem from one of the bushes. He peeled away the bark as a person would peel a banana, and chewed on the soft, woody fiber inside.

The chimpanzees were very noisy as they moved along. The adults barked and grunted to each other; infants whimpered; and the older children raced around and around, playing tag, wrestling, biting, screaming, and yelling. Usually, this "mothers' group" would have been much quieter because of the need to protect the helpless infants from the predators that lived in the forest. But this morning was different.

For several weeks, the group had been travelling to the fig trees that grew in a meadow near the night's nesting area. Figs were the chimpanzees' favorite food, and as they ripened day by day the animals became more excited.

Now, as the chimpanzees neared the meadow, they raced
along the trails and bounded through the underbrush,
galloping along on all four legs. They leaped ditches and
small streams, jumping with arms and legs spread out, then,
while in mid-air, swinging their legs under their bodies to
land feet-first.

Wild hooting and drumming came from the meadow.
Other chimpanzees already were there. The sound was like
a wild dance with all the dancers yelling and screaming.
BOOM-BOOM-BOOM! HOO-HOO-HOO! Toto's group
answered the calls and dashed even faster down the aisles
between the trees. They burst through the screen of trees
that bordered the fig meadow. At the meadow's edge, adult
chimpanzees were pounding with their hands and feet on
the exposed roots, called plank buttresses, of ironwood
trees. BOOM-BOOM-BOOM! The chimpanzees' heads
were thrown back and their eyes were closed as they hooted
and hollered in time to the wild drumming. Then they
bounded toward the fig trees to gorge themselves and others
took their places at the "drums."

There were six or seven fig trees growing in the meadow, and the fruit was ripe. A strong, sickly-sweet aroma
hung in the air, attracting hordes of buzzing, biting, suck-
ing insects. But the chimpanzees didn't seem to mind. They
sat among the branches stuffing their mouths full of the
juicy yellow fruit. They dropped half-eaten figs to the
ground, where they were squashed by the stamping, run-

Young chimpanzees. They often play together when their group is feeding or resting.

ning, hooting chimpanzees. Over thirty of the forest's fifty or so chimpanzees were in the fig trees, and more arrived each minute.

When Toto and his group broke out of the forest, they whooped and hooted as they saw old friends from other groups. They ran to each other, threw their arms around each other's shoulders, kissed, and touched. They grinned and chattered, then bounded into the trees to gobble and grunt, drip and squash in the general excitement and confusion of the feast.

After eating his fill, Toto broke away from the adults to join a group of youngsters his own age who were playing in the trees. He grabbed a little male by the arm, nipped him, and fled as the victim turned on him. The two chased each other back and forth through the trees, slipping on ripe figs, upsetting adults, falling from the branches to squeal and grin and roll. Toto was nipped a bit too hard and ran whimpering to his mother. She looked up, patted him on the head, and returned to eating figs. Satisfied, Toto bounded away searching for more play.

His sister moved timidly away from her mother's chest. It was the three-month-old baby's first adventure into the world. At first she moved very slowly and carefully. She released her hold on her mother's hair, one hand at a time, crawled onto a fig-laden branch, and sat wrapped around an upright twig. She touched one of the ripe figs, licked her finger, grimaced, and reached back to touch her mother for assurance. The mother patted her. The baby stood on her wobbly legs and reached up to grab a small branch that grew above her head. She swung free, twisting and turning as she hung by both her skinny arms. It was all fun and the baby seemed to enjoy it, but only until she realized that she was trapped. Her arms were too weak to pull her onto the upper branch and her legs too short for her to stand on the lower one. She screamed. Her mother swung around and scooped her from the perch.

After about two hours of feeding, the chimpanzees

were full. The hooting, whooping, hollering, and drumming faded away as the apes sat quietly playing with the figs. They picked one here or there, squashed it between their fingers, perhaps bit into it, but more often than not simply dropped it to the ground, where it joined the heap of half-eaten fruit that already lay there. The older children had tired of their play and sat beside their mothers. The very young had fallen asleep. A quiet, broken only by the hordes of insects that buzzed around the spoiling fruit, hung over the meadow. It was as though the chimpanzees were waiting for something to happen.

At length, a large male stood on the branch where he had been feeding. He yawned, a sign that he was bored and restless. Then he dropped to the ground and moved toward the edge of the meadow. He was one of the dominant males among the forest's chimpanzees, five feet tall, weighing more than one hundred and sixty pounds, twenty-one years old, and in the prime of his life. His thick coat of long, black hair glistened in the sunlight as he walked. His arms and shoulders were hard and powerful; his legs were short and bowed, with broad, turned-in feet that were as tough and wrinkled as old leather. The big male walked on all fours, his feet flat on the ground and the knuckles of his fingers supporting the forward part of his body.

Because he was a dominant animal in the group, the other chimpanzees made way for him as he approached. The males crouched and gave out small, high-pitched screams, a signal that they recognized their leader's position. He patted them or hooted softly as he passed. The childless females and older juveniles acknowledged him. Only those females with very young children and the children themselves were immune from the ritual of greeting the master. The big male tickled or patted the babies and ignored the mothers.

When he reached the border of the meadow, he stopped and looked back toward the other chimpanzees. He hooted softly, calling the animals to him. Then he moved into the forest and pounded on an ironwood tree. BOOM-BOOM! Two of the chimpanzees jumped out of the fig trees and ran to join him.

Although the forest's fifty to sixty chimpanzees lived in seven small groups, only the mothers' group stayed together for any length of time. All the others changed constantly. The chimpanzees lived and travelled in these smaller groups as a matter of convenience in food gathering. Since everybody knew everybody else, members switched from group to group, often several times in one day. The groups contacted each other often as they moved through the forest, and it was simple for a member of one to wander off with another.

So when the big male left the fig-tree meadow, two of the childless females of Toto's group decided to move off with him. They were seven years old and approaching maturity, a time when male company became more impor-

tant than the security they had known with their mothers.
But leavetaking wasn't easy for them. They ran back and
forth between the mothers' group and the edge of the forest
where the big male waited. They squealed and sought the
comfort of their mothers, then dashed for the forest, only
to stop, look back over their shoulders, and run back to the
tree. Finally, the big male, as though disgusted with all
this nonsense, moved away, and the females fell into line
behind him. Although it appeared that they were leaving,
never to return, the fact was that they would see their
mothers the following day at the fig tree. They might even
choose to rejoin the old group temporarily. Chimpanzee
society was very flexible; the only stable families were
those of mothers and their dependent children. Everyone
else was free to come and go as he pleased. Any one of the
mature males might be the father of any of the children,
and it was highly unlikely that a brother and sister had the
same father. The dominant males usually had their pick of
the females, but if a female chose not to show her attentions to a particular male, even if he were dominant, she
was not forced to do so. And she was free to join another
band if the males in her group didn't please her. Even the
old chimpanzees could change groups, although they usually chose the mothers, probably because this group moved
more slowly than the others. So two very old, lame grand-
mothers stayed behind when the other chimpanzees broke
away and left the fig trees.

As the day grew hotter, Toto's mother led her group into the tall grass that grew beside a stream on the edge of the meadow. There she flopped onto the ground and fell asleep. A few of the other chimpanzees built crude nests in the trees, but most simply lay in the deep grass, for nest-building was primarily for nighttime sleeping. After a brief period of chasing and wrestling with the other youngsters, Toto curled up against his mother and slept.

All of the forest's animals seemed to sleep away the day's hottest hours. The birds grew still; Tembo the elephant, deep in his swampy home, shifted from foot to foot as he dozed; Nyati the buffalo lay cool in the mud under a tree, contentedly chewing his cud; the python had caught a hyrax and now lay coiled beneath a bush, digesting its meal; Chui the leopard crouched over the dead body of Nende the duiker. She had caught the little antelope as it slept among the bushes that grew along the forest floor, and although the duiker was incredibly fast, so fast that it seemed to dive into the safety of the undergrowth, the cat was an experienced hunter, and in a flash it was all over.

Later that day, Toto almost stepped on Chui. It happened this way:

There had been a heavy rain in the afternoon, certainly not unusual for the tropics, but the chimpanzees never seemed to get used to these storms. During the first part of the rain, a miserable drizzle that soaked everything in the forest, the adults crouched on the ground, letting the water pour down their backs. The very young babies, like Toto's sister, stayed warm and dry, huddled against their mothers' chests. But Toto and the older children played wildly in the rain. They ran back and forth, chased each other through the trees, wrestled, and slipped in the mud of the forest floor. During one chase through the trees, Toto swung around a branch and there was the leopard, Chui, crouched over the duiker, which she had dragged aloft as leopards usually do with their kill. The chimpanzee screamed in fear and fled. And the cat was as shocked as the little ape. She knew from experience that if she stayed, there would be more than a dozen excited, biting, scream- ing adult chimpanzees to contend with, so she slipped away in the opposite direction.

Except for man, leopards were the chimpanzees' main enemy, and though the big, tree-climbing cats killed an infant or a very old animal once in a while, if the chim- panzees stayed healthy and active they had little to fear from the leopard or any non-human predator.

But they had much to fear from man. There was a long history of hatred among the natives of the area for the chimpanzees, whom they called, "Soko-mutu," meaning "The man with the ugly face who should not be." In truth, the apes did little to make the people love them. Once in a while, especially in the lean season, they raided the na- tives' gardens and tore out yams and maize, eating part of the crop and destroying weeks of work. But if the chimpanzees stayed in the forest, they had little to fear, for most of the people avoided the dark, pathless jungle. Only those who worked for the lumber companies had direct contact with the chimpanzees. These contacts, infrequent as they might be, usually were disasterous for the apes. The people were protein-starved and looked on any animal as a source of meat.

In cutting the forests in which the chimpanzees lived, man indirectly killed the animals. One of the worst practices was poisoning the fig trees. To the lumber companies, they were "weed trees," taking up space that could be better used to grow the economically valuable mahogany. But the fig trees produced much of the fruit which the chimpanzees ate, and by killing these trees the lumber companies were taking away part of the apes' food supply. The chimpanzees were primarily fruit eaters, and figs were their main food.

During the forest's dry season, when no fruit was ripe, the apes ate leaves, stems, buds, insects, bird's eggs, and even the birds themselves. Then their normally wild, noisy antics stopped and the chimpanzees moved about quietly, seldom calling back and forth. But when the various fruits were ripe, all the forests' groups gathered at the trees—the one with little red fruits that tasted like ginger; the igeria, which grew in the swamps where Tembo the elephant lived; and, of course, the figs. One group would announce its finds to the others by hooting, whooping, and

drumming on the ironwood trees. The forests would ring
with the sound and the natives would say that "Old Soko-
mutu is having his carnival."

The chimpanzees were among the most adaptable of
the anthropoid apes. Uncounted thousands lived from the
Atlantic coast of central Africa eastward to Uganda and
Tanzania. Most lived in thick tropical rain forests, but some
moved among more open woodlands, and others lived in
the mountains at ten thousand feet above sea level. One
species, the pygmy chimpanzee, or Bonobo, was much

Pygmy chimpanzee adult.   SAN DIEGO ZOO

smaller than the others. He lived south of the Congo River, separated by it from the rest of the chimpanzees. And since none of the chimpanzees could swim, and disliked entering the water, the Bonobos' isolation was complete.

In all of their different environments, chimpanzees fared quite well. Those who lived in the deep forests ate a great amount of fruit, supplemented with insects and birds' eggs. Those who were woodland dwellers ate leaves, buds, wild celery, and other vegetation. They also killed and ate small animals now and then. And they captured termites, the insects which build tall mounds of dirt in which to live. Termites were not found in old forests, but abounded in more open woods. In order to capture these delicacies, a chimpanzee would choose a twig or blade of grass that was long and slender. If it were not quite the right shape, he might nibble away the bark or narrow the blade of grass with his teeth. Then he would squat beside a termite mound and pick away the soil until he uncovered a tunnel. He inserted the twig into the tunnel. The termite soldiers, assuming that the colony had been invaded, would clamp their pincers onto the twig. When the chimpanzee felt them biting, he would withdraw the twig, now covered with termites, and lick it clean.

The fact that the chimpanzees make and use a tool, even one so crude as a twig, should not be surprising. Among all animals, they are considered next to man in intelligence. One authority suggests that perhaps one of

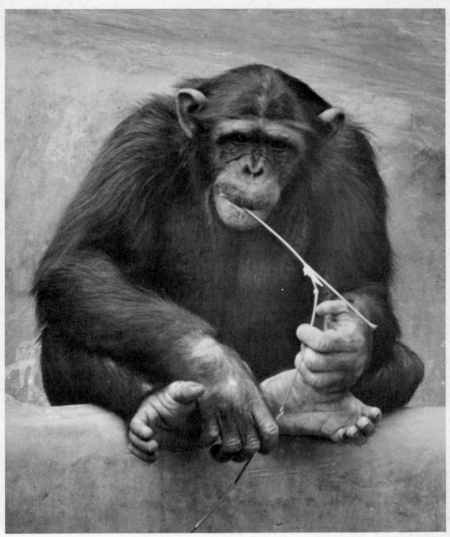

Chimpanzees often make crude tools from twigs or blades of grass to help them get food.

the only reasons that the chimpanzees didn't move out of the forests as man did was that man beat them to the move, and the apes weren't capable of competing with him on the grasslands. But the chimpanzees developed a high degree of social sense in their jungle homes. A mere squeal of pain or a whimper would bring an infant's mother running. And a call of alarm from a member of the group sent the rest of the apes either fleeing or coming to help. This is what happened when Toto ran into the leopard.

He screamed in fright, and in a matter of seconds the adults were clustered around, ready to either snatch Toto away from danger or to fight the leopard if necessary. Perhaps because chimpanzees are so high strung (they are the noisiest and most active of all the great apes), they also can be the most vicious and easily angered. They seldom fight among themselves, but when they do the battles are violent.

During the leopard incident, the drizzling rain had become a full-fledged storm. Wind tore at the trees and whipped the rain through the forest. Broken branches crashed to the ground. Vines swayed back and forth. Close by, an old mahogany toppled over, taking several smaller trees with it to the forest's floor.

The fury of the storm got to the chimpanzees, already worked up by Toto's cries of alarm. From a nearby hill, the group led by the big male called excitedly. HOO! HOO! HOO! The mothers ran to join them. They burst into a clearing where the other chimpanzees were gathered —the males by themselves and the females and their youngsters off to one side. The leader milled about nervously at the top of the hill. Suddenly, with a yell, he jumped into a tree. He tore away a branch and dropped back to the ground. He dashed down the hill, dragging and swinging the branch behind him. HOO! HOO! At the hill's bottom, he leaped into another tree, swung around the trunk, then ran back up the hill. All of the males hooted and leaped in excitement. They charged down the hill, brandishing branches they had torn from trees. At the bottom of the hill, they swung around a tree trunk and raced back to the top of the hill. Again and again. Wilder and wilder.

Then it was over. The wind died away; the rain slackened; the sun poked through the clouds, and as quickly as the chimpanzees' "rain dance" had begun, it ended. The big male stopped dashing back and forth, looked about, and shook the water from his back much as a dog shakes himself. He wandered into the forest and began eating. Gradually the two groups—the mothers and those who moved with the big male—parted company. Toto's mother led her group slowly up the hill, feeding as she went, and by the time she reached the area in which she chose to nest that night, all the bellies in the group were round and full.

During that day, the chimpanzees had travelled

about one mile inside their seven-square-mile homeland. Later in the year, after the fruit was gone, they might have to move three or four miles in one day just to find food. But during the good times when figs or igeria were ripe, the group travelled very little, really only from one tree to another. And when they moved more than a few yards, even in the thick forest, they swung down from the trees and walked or ran along the ground. Yet when evening came, they climbed back into the trees to build their sleeping nests. In this respect, chimpanzees are the most flexible of all the great apes—not truly ground-living creatures as the gorillas, and certainly far less confined to the treetops than the orangutans or gibbons.

Toto's mother climbed into a large mahogany tree. About eighty feet off the forest's floor, she began building a nest. First she bent several stout branches beneath her and pressed them down with the weight of her body. Then she broke off smaller branches to use as padding, and placed them onto the platform she had made. Still not satisfied, she gathered handfuls of leaves and scattered them around the nest. The entire nest-building chore took her about five minutes. As darkness fell over the forest, she climbed into the nest and curled up with her baby at her breast. Somewhere down the hill, a chimpanzee hooted softly. Toto answered; then, without a backward glance at the forest, now dark and gloomy, he climbed into the nest, snuggled against his mother's warm, hairy body, and in a few minutes was sound asleep.

CHAPTER 3

Kinguti

EACH MORNING, Kinguti the mountain gorilla and his small group leave their sleeping area and spend the daylight hours browsing through the rain forest that covers the eastern border of the Congo Republic in central Africa. Eight volcanic peaks rise from this forest, forming a mountain chain called Virunga, meaning "high mountains that reach the clouds" in the local language. Two of the peaks are still active, occasionally sending streams of molten lava down their slopes to engulf the forests and villages below. All the others are extinct. At night, masses of cold air slide away from the highest and drift into the forests below. Then the temperature among the trees drops to the freezing point.

But by ten o'clock in the morning, the forest lies warm under the tropical sun. Even among the hagenia trees, growing at eight thousand feet above sea level, the air is mild, for the Virungas rise very close to the earth's equator.

Adult silverback gorilla.

The peaks shimmer on the skyline and the forest canopy lies hot and quiet, a dark green carpet that stretches unbroken from the horizon to the bases of the peaks.

One morning, a touraco flew into a small clearing in a part of the forest growing on the slopes of one of the peaks. A hagenia tree, thick-trunked and sixty feet tall, grew on the clearing's upper edge. The touraco flew to it, landed on a low branch that sprouted straight out from the trunk, and began preening its dull green body feathers. As it arranged each of its feathers, the bird watched a beam of sunlight a few feet away. Suddenly, an insect flitted through the beam. Its wings caught the sunlight and for a brief moment it glittered like a silver jewel. The bird saw the insect and swooped down from the limb. The sunbeam seemed to explode into scarlet and green light as the bird flashed through on its brilliant red wings. It caught the insect, flew back to the limb, and resumed preening itself. The bird had visited the tree for several days, drawn there by the insects that fluttered through the sunbeam. It considered the clearing its private hunting reserve and drove away other birds who ventured near.

After several minutes of feeding, the touraco heard a rustling in the grass that grew at the base of the hagenia. Assuming the sound came from a rival bird, it raised the crest on its head, fluffed out its body feathers, and prepared to defend its territory. But the huge, black head that pushed through the grass could hardly belong to any bird.

The touraco squawked in fear and fluttered away, leaving the clearing to Kinguti the mountain gorilla.

Kinguti stuck his head farther through the screen of grass. It was a massive head, covered with coarse, black hair and topped by a prominent bump, called a sagittal crest, which provided an anchor for the gorilla's jaw muscles. A huge, overhanging brow almost hid his eyes, which were set deep in his head and seemed like two pinpoints of light peering out from a dark cave. Kinguti had a flat, broad, bridgeless nose with flaring, forward-pointing nostrils. His mouth was full and protruding, with thin, expressive lips. And his ears, although manlike, were very small for such a huge head and were almost hidden by hair.

Before entering the clearing, Kinguti carefully studied the scene. Despite his formidable appearance, he was a gentle creature and very timid. He knew this clearing, since it was at one edge of his group's territory, but he had no way of knowing what other animal might have claimed it since he had last visited it several months earlier. Maybe the neighboring troop of gorillas led by Splitlip had invaded; perhaps a leopard was crouching in the grass, tensed to leap on one of the babies; or there might be native cattle grazing in the clearing, driven onto the mountain by their owners. Kinguti looked around carefully. But, except for the hagenia tree, the clearing was empty.

The hagenia with its moss-covered branches dominated the clearing. At its base, bright green grass and a clump of wild celery shared the sunshine. A thick growth of pale bamboo rimmed the clearing's lower edge. On one side, a small gully protected the clearing from the forest, but on the other side, the bushes and saplings were slowly moving in.

Satisfied that the clearing was safe, Kinguti pushed through the grass. He was an immense animal, the largest of all primates. His head seemed to squat, neckless, on a pair of broad shoulders. He had long, powerful arms and short, but equally powerful, legs. His bulky torso was almost completely covered with hair, and his huge, round belly swung beneath him as he walked four-legged across the clearing. Kinguti weighed four hundred pounds and supported his weight on the soles of his feet and the heavy calluses that grew on the knuckles of each hand. His knuckles left a print almost six inches wide in the earth. (A man's hand, by comparison, is only a bit over three inches in width.) His footprint was eleven inches long and six wide. A man's is equally long, but only about four inches wide.

As he moved across the clearing toward the hagenia and the wild celery growing at its base, Kinguti stood erect. He was more than six feet tall, and his arms hung below his knees. He waddled through the beam of sunlight in which the touraco had hunted insects. The hair on his body, head, arms, and legs glistened bluish-black in the sunlight. Because he was a mature male, thirteen years old, he had a patch of gray hair, called a saddle, growing across his back. In the sunlight it gleamed like silver. Mature male gorillas are called silverbacks because of this feature. The skin on Kinguti's chest was a deep charcoal gray, heavily muscled and almost bare. The palms of his hands and the soles of his feet were totally hairless, black, and deeply creased.

When he reached the hagenia, Kinguti looked back over his shoulder and grunted softly. At the signal, another gorilla, a female, pushed through the grass. She was smaller than Kinguti and lacked his silverback marking. Otherwise, she looked much the same. She walked three-legged and held a pinkish-gray baby to her chest with her free arm. Unlike other apes, newborn gorillas do not have the strength to cling to their mother's bodies, so they must be carried for several weeks. The baby was covered with a sparse coat of soft, black hair, except on its rump, where it had a tuft of snow-white hair. Although the rest of the baby hair would be replaced in a matter of months by a thick, coarse coat, the little rump tuft would last for four years.

Behind the female and her baby, several other gorillas filed into the clearing. Four were females, one childless, one held a young infant and two had two-year-olds riding jockey-style on their backs. The babies clung to their mothers' hair with hands and feet and their full, round bellies bounced up and down each time the females stepped forward. Three immature males, called blackbacks, trailed behind. Ranging in age from seven to nine years, they were smaller than Kinguti, still not grown enough to be silverbacks, and on only the oldest did a few white hairs mark the place where the saddle would eventually appear. Behind them, a female of great age limped into the clearing. More than thirty years old, she was almost completely gray and moved with great difficulty. She was badly crippled with arthritis, and she coughed constantly. Finally, two silverback males entered the clearing. Each was almost Kinguti's size; each was mature and in his prime. But neither held a position of leadership in the group.

The twelve gorillas began eating as soon as they had gathered at the base of the hagenia tree. Some squatted on their haunches, some wandered slowly around the edge of the clearing, and others lay in the sun. They grabbed handfuls of grass, tender young stalks of wild celery, and bits of vine. They crammed their mouths full, chewed noisily, then reached out to sweep in still more food. Stripping the spines from nettles with their tough hands, they used their fingers to open the stalks, then tore away the soft inner pith. One of the immature males wandered to a rotting log, ripped away the tough bark as easily as if it were made of tissue paper, and licked up the whitish fluid that flowed out. The two infants nursed at their mothers' breasts. One of the two-year-olds came up to his mother, nursed briefly, then walked away. He passed close by one of the

Baby gorillas. They are playful and much more active than the adults.

nursing infants and reached out to grab its foot. The mother pushed him gently away. He saw the other two-year-old sitting beside its mother, playing at making a nest. With one hand the young gorilla bent over blades of grass and with the other pressed them into shape around his body. Suddenly, the first two-year-old pounced into the middle of the play nest, and the two youngsters started wrestling. They bit and pulled at each other, rolled across the clearing, and bumped into the feeding adults. The adults ignored them. One of the youngsters broke free and ran to the hagenia tree, the other gorilla hard on his heels. They clambered into the tree, swatting at each other. One lost his hold, and tumbled to the ground. With a squeal of pain, the young gorilla dashed to its mother and began to nurse. She patted its head. Soothed, it returned to the rough-and-tumble play with its young friend.

After stuffing themselves for an hour, the gorillas became more selective in their feeding. They purred loudly as they plucked a spear of grass here, a choice bit of wild celery there. Their bellies grew hard and round, and by eleven o'clock the apes were merely sitting or lying in the grass. Kinguti moved to the base of the hagenia tree, curled up on his side, and, with one arm under his head, fell asleep. Taking the cue from their leader, the rest of the group also rested. Some sprawled on their backs, soaking in the sun. One built a crude nest of grass and twigs, crouched on his hands and knees within it, and went to sleep. The two-year-olds gave up their game of follow-the-leader around and around the hagenia and returned to their mothers, where they curled up to sleep. The clearing became quiet, with only the rumbling of the contented gorillas' stomachs breaking the silence.

While the gorillas slept, a cloud made up of water

vapor drawn from the forest by the heat appeared in the sky. Beginning as a filmy white wisp, it grew rapidly, spread outward, and in a matter of minutes had obscured the sun and was lapping at the slopes of the Virunga peaks. It shrouded the giant senecios that grew at an elevation of thirteen thousand feet on the mountain. These twisted, grotesque plants, looking like prehistoric trees, grew more than twenty feet tall. They, and other species of equally weird-looking plants, provided food for the gorillas during the animals' rare visits to these high altitudes. Below the senecios, the mist lay across old lava flows which had spilled from the peaks when they were active volcanoes. The gorillas avoided these barren slopes of the mountain, for they were essentially forest animals and seldom ventured beyond its borders.

As the cloud grew, it moved farther down the mountainside, invading the forest where Kinguti and his group lay sleeping. Pale mist settled onto the clearing and covered the trees, vines, and stands of bamboo. The dark green leaves and vines hung motionless and black against the gray background. The yellowish-green of the bamboo dulled to gray. The moss on the tree branches grew wet and black. The gorillas' coats, so blue-black and glossy in the sunlight, became lusterless and soggy, and the animals' natural odor, musty and somewhat sweet, hung heavy in the still air.

Then it began to rain. Water dripped from the leaves

and ran down the vines. Small pools formed in the crotches of tree branches and in the footprints of elephants and buffalo. When the pools overflowed, rivulets formed and ran down the hillside. They reached the clearing and seeped under the sleeping Kinguti. The gorilla turned in his sleep, trying to find a dry place on the cold, soggy ground. The water trickled across the clearing and into the small gully formed over the years by runoff. A stream began to run in the normally dry gully. As the rain continued, the stream grew larger until it was three feet across, splashing its way over old lava stones and tearing at the vines and grasses that choked the gully's bottom. Farther downstream, the water poured from the gully and joined other streams that drained the mountain's slope. The river that was formed would flow on, until it emptied into the Lualaba, which in turn would help form the Congo, Africa's second longest river. And one day, more than twenty-five hundred miles from their beginnings on the slopes of the Virunga volcanoes, the drops of water that had seeped under Kinguti as he lay sleeping would leave the land-locked river and become part of the Atlantic Ocean.

But all Kinguti knew about the rain was that the wet ground had finally awakened him. Grunting in annoyance, he sat up. Although rain was an almost daily experience, he, like all other apes, disliked it immensely. He got to his feet and left the nest. Nearby, snug and dry in the shelter of the hagenia tree, one of the blackbacked males lay sleeping.

Kinguti walked over, squatted beside him, and nudged him
out of the shelter. The young male came awake, ready to
protest. But when he saw Kinguti, he submitted meekly and
moved into the rain. He walked to the childless female who
was sitting, partially protected from the drizzle, under one
of the hagenia's branches. The young male tried to evict
her by nudging, as Kinguti had done to him. But the
female, rather than submitting, cuffed him alongside the
head, and the male gave up and squatted wretchedly in
the rain. It would be at least two or three years before he
could dominate even the females in the group. In time,
when Kinguti died, he might take command of the group.
Even the presence of two other silverbacks did not assure
that they, rather than some other male, would become
dominant. In the tightly-knit gorilla society, where groups
stayed together for years at a time, mere physical size or
strength was no guarantee that a mature male would take
command. Several other qualities also determined who
would assume leadership; they were probably intelligence, the courage to stand up to opponents, and even the
cockiness to simply take over the role of leader. Nor was
leadership totally confined to the dominant male. For instance, the first animal to sense danger, even if he were
quite young, could send the group dashing for safety. But
in day-to-day decisions—where to feed, what direction to
travel, when and where to sleep—the dominant silverback
was undisputed king.

So, even though the gorillas preferred to leave the clearing and move into the relative shelter of the forest, as long as Kinguti stayed in his place, the rest of the group sat miserable and wet in the rain. They drew their knees to their chins, clasped their arms around their legs, hunched their heads forward, and simply let the rain soak their backs. Mothers with infants held their young ones tightly against their chests, keeping them warm and dry. And even the two-year-olds clung to their mothers, protected by the great, black bodies.

Rain was a common experience for the gorillas, and usually they endured it with nothing more serious than a cold. But to the old female of the group, already ill and lame, each wetting of her body by rain meant even more sickness. Because she was so old, whatever position of dominance she had held among the females in earlier years had long ago passed to younger members of the group. So she could command no warm shelter from the weather, and sat completely exposed. Her thin, gray hair offered no real protection, and water ran down her bare head and back. She coughed continuously, and her feeble body shivered in the damp chill of the afternoon. But none of the other gorillas seemed to notice her as she squatted at the very edge of the clearing, away from the group's center.

By midafternoon, the rain ended and the mist gradually lifted from the forest. One by one, the gorillas shook themselves dry and began feeding. Kinguti moved

to the bamboo that grew on the clearing's lower border and started digging the tender, young shoots from
the ground. He scooped the dirt aside, exposing the un-
developed bamboo, jerked each shoot free, stripped it of
its outer layer, and ate the inner meat as though it were a
banana. In the forest's dry season, when the bamboo sent
up few new shoots, the gorillas avoided eating the plant,
for then it was tough. But during the rains when new
growth seemed to sprout overnight, the tender pith of the
bamboo was among the gorillas' favorite food. After satis-
fying his hunger, Kinguti went to the edge of the gully,
leaned over, and began eating the soil. This earth, very
rich in minerals, supplied the gorillas' need for salt.

While he was at the salt lick, Kinguti heard a group
of chimpanzees passing close by in the forest. His hearing
was much more acute than a human's and he recognized
the chimpanzees' yells and screamings at once. Not only
chimps, but several species of monkeys lived in the forest
with the gorillas, and since they did not compete with the
gorilla for food and space, that is, did not occupy the same
ecological niche, they were not Kinguti's enemies. In fact,
he had very few enemies. Of all the other animals in the
forest—the antelope, elephants, buffalo, birds, and cats—
only the leopard was a foe.

There was one other—man. He was avoided at
all costs. Occasionally Kinguti ventured into a native's
garden and stole maize, yams, or banana trees, but
these were lightning-fast attacks, and at the first sound or

sight of man, the gorilla and his group dashed into the safety of the forest. The gorillas were completely protected by law from hunting, but the meat-starved natives still killed one now and then for food. In earlier years, before they were protected by law, countless animals were killed for sport or captured for zoos. Yet, even with the law's protection, man remained the gorillas' main enemy. He cut the forests for lumber and, even worse, grazed his cattle on the same plants that the gorillas ate. Among the natives in the area, the ownership of cattle was a mark of wealth. The more cattle a person owned, no matter how scrawny and half-starved the animals might be, the richer he was in the eyes of his tribe. And the cattle themselves were not judged by the quality of their meat or milk, for the natives did not slaughter or milk them; their value lay in the size of their horns. The larger the horns were, the more valuable were the animals. So, despite the protection given by guards who tried to keep the herds out of the gorillas' country, cattle continued to move in and ruin the land. They, and the rapidly increasing human population that surrounded the mountain gorillas' home—among the most densely populated part of Africa—could spell the end of Kinguti and the other gorillas living in the shadow of the Virunga volcanoes. One scientist feels that they will be extinct by the end of this century. Today, only between five thousand and fifteen thousand of them still exist, living in an area of about thirty-five thousand square miles.

But the gorillas have been decreasing in population

for many years, and their present low number is not totally
because of man. Six hundred-fifty miles west of Kinguti's
mountain home, another gorilla population lives in the low-
lying, humid rain forests of the western Congo Republic
and neighboring countries. They are called lowland gorillas
and are very much like Kinguti; in fact, they are members
of the same species. There are probably many more lowland than mountain gorillas, possibly because they live in
such remote, impenetrable forests that they cannot be
killed or captured easily. Thousands of years ago, the two
types undoubtedly lived together in the continuous belt
of trees that grew across the breadth of the Congo basin.
But a slight change in climate, perhaps in the amount of
rainfall, took place at the forests' northern limits. It was
just enough to shift the border between forest and grassland slightly southward. Gorillas do not like open country,
so they moved back with the forests. But, as they were
forced south, they encountered major rivers flowing from
the north. And these rivers acted as barriers between the
groups, for gorillas cannot swim, and will not voluntarily
enter water. Over thousands of years, the two populations
developed into two types, lowland and mountain; and their
numbers probably remained steady until modern man with
his guns, livestock, and industry came on the scene.

But despite man's poaching, his cattle that ruined
the land, and his lumbering operations that destroyed the
forests, he was not totally responsible for the gorillas' sorry

plight. In fact, quite accidentally, he sometimes helped them. The natives who farmed the area, unlike those who owned and grazed cattle, cleared small sections of the forest for their gardens. They felled a block of trees, then burned the wood and undergrowth. In the small clearings that re- sulted, they planted their crops—maize, yams, and bananas. But, exposed to the direct sunlight, the open land was soon leached of its minerals, and after three or four years was useless for farming. The natives abandoned it and moved elsewhere to cut and burn. In the old clearing, the forest quickly moved in, and in two or three years the second growth, rich with vines, grass, and herbs, provided the gorillas with food.

In time, the small clearing where Kinguti and his group were resting and feeding would revert to old, pri- mary forest. Small trees and bushes would be crowded out by stronger trees which would soar more than one hundred feet into the air. Their tops would interlace and the sun- loving plants would disappear. Then, without food plants to lure them, the gorillas would avoid the clearing and move into younger sections of the forest. But while the clearing passed through its growth phase of hagenia, grass, and bamboo, it was one of the apes' favorite spots. They visited it regularly during the rainy seasons when the bam- boo put out new growth, often staying in the area for days at a time. And since the clearing lay along one edge of the group's home range, an area of about four square miles, it was visited by other groups as well. One such group wandered into the clearing late in the afternoon.

By three o'clock the sky was clear once more. Water from the day's rain still dripped from leaves and vines, but the sun shone and Kinguti and the rest of his group lolled in its warmth, eating and grooming themselves. Mothers groomed their young, who resisted violently; females groomed other females, and, occasionally, Kinguti and the other silverbacked males groomed one of the youngsters. The apes shoved their faces close to the arm or back or rump being groomed, as though they were very near-sighted. They poked and picked at the hair of the other animal, searching for dirt, seeds, loose bits of skin, and other foreign matter. But, overall, the mutual grooming seemed less enthusiastic and not so important a social affair as among other species of apes, particularly the chimpan-zees. The gorillas' main activity was eating, and even after stuffing themselves, they continued nibbling contentedly until the other group showed up.

One of the young blackbacked males was the first to hear the intruders. He raised his head, peered in the direc-tion of the cracking branches and rustling grass, and gave out a series of low-pitched hoots, then growled, as though warning the rest of his group. They snapped alert and looked toward the source of the noise.

The grass parted as half-a-dozen gorillas entered the clearing, led by a large silverback with a split lip that pulled his mouth into a sneer. They stopped just inside the clearing, watching Kinguti's group. Splitlip stood on all fours, his arms bent outward at the elbows and his back straight, as though showing off for Kinguti and his group. The females and younger males sat quietly behind him, waiting. Splitlip moved a few feet into the clearing. Kinguti rose from the salt lick and strode four-legged up the hill. He stopped about eight feet from Splitlip. The two silverbacks stood silently, staring at each other. One of the young males from the new group got up, wandered among Kinguti's group, sniffed curiously at the infants and two-year-olds, then ambled back into his own group. None of the gorillas paid any attention to him. The two silverbacks continued staring at each other. This direct staring was a threat gesture which excited the two apes, and unless one of them looked aside, the tension would build still further. It was not unlike two boys who try to stare down each other, seeming to say with their eyes, "I'm tougher than you are."

Suddenly, Kinguti started hooting. It began as a series of low, clear calls that grew faster and louder until they blended into one penetrating sound that rang through the clearing. The other gorillas of both groups stirred restlessly. Kinguti became more tense. He plucked a leaf and put it between his lips, as though by this eating gesture he could release some of the tension. He leaped to his feet, tore away a handful of vegetation, and threw it wildly into the air. Standing fully erect, he began to beat his chest with

his hands. POKA-POKA-POKA-POKA! The drumming
exploded through the forest. Females scooped up their
young and scampered out of the way. Kinguti kicked out
at the air with one foot and pounded his chest more rapidly.
Suddenly, he dropped to all fours and ran sideways, slapping at the vegetation and tearing it from the ground. As a
final gesture, he thumped the ground hard, once with his
hand. Then he sat and stared at Splitlip, as though saying, "Now get out of my territory!"

Splitlip rose. He roared, slapped his chest as Kinguti
had done, dashed around the clearing, slapping and tearing
at the plants, then returned to stand staring at Kinguti.
Suddenly, his feet firmly planted on the ground he thrust
his body forward. Kinguti rose and charged at him, but
he stopped two feet short of Splitlip's face. Splitlip rose,
slapped his chest, raced around the clearing, and charged
again, this time coming eye-to-eye with the other gorilla.

It went on for almost half-an-hour. First one, then
the other silverback would rise, slap his chest, dash around
madly, charge, stop and sit staring at the other. But never
once, in their wild displaying, did they come into physical
contact. Nor would they, for gorillas rarely fight.

About one hundred years ago, a white explorer
named Du Chaillu encountered the huge apes, witnessed
their excited displays, and wrote that he had seen a "gorilla
beating his chest in *rage*." With these few words, the myth
of the "ferocious" gorilla was born. Fantastic stories were

SAN DIEGO ZOO
Young male gorilla beating his chest.

invented in which gorillas attacked and killed people or stole babies and women. Movies pictured gorillas as villains. And over the years, even among scientists who should have known better, this distorted, inaccurate image grew about the great ape who lived in the dark forests of Africa.

The truth was much less dramatic. Kinguti and the other gorillas, both lowland and mountain, were gentle creatures who wanted nothing more than to be left alone to feed, rest, and sleep. When they met groups with whom they were not friendly, there might be a great display of chest beating, running, roaring, and so forth, but only in rare instances did the bluffs end in actual fighting.

As a matter of fact, although Kinguti and Splitlip disliked each other and always met as enemies, they soon tired of their game. After half an hour, Splitlip swung away with a final roar, and led his group out of the clearing. The two groups had met before and would meet again, for the gorillas constantly moved, and each meeting probably would be the noisy, blustering affair this one had been. There were two other groups living on the mountain, and meetings with them were casual and friendly. These groups intermingled from time to time and almost seemed to ignore each other, except for the curious, young males who peacefully investigated each new stranger.

As Splitlip and his group left the clearing, the members of Kinguti's group, aroused by the two leaders' displayings, became noisy. Several beat their chests, roared in the deep, explosive way of gorillas, or simply hooted. One of the immature males strutted stiff-legged along a rotting log as though saying, "See how tough our group is!" But the log split under his weight, dumping the gorilla on the ground and exposing the milky-white fluid that such logs often contain. The young blackback immediately forgot his big performance and turned to lapping up the fluid. The two-year-olds climbed into the hagenia and began wrestling on a branch. The infants, buried in the safety of their mothers' arms during the recent encounter, squirmed restlessly, wanting to nurse. Kinguti went back to the salt lick. Peace and quiet returned to the group.

Later in the afternoon, they again encountered a gorilla from outside their group. He was one of three or four silverbacks who wandered alone around the forest. Once in a while such a mature male would drift away from his group to live by himself.

The silverback announced his arrival well before any of Kinguti's group saw him. He roared and immediately was answered by Kinguti and the other males. But unlike Splitlip, the loner was accepted into the group as though he were a member and was soon ignored. He would stay with them for a week or so, and when he left, the childless female and one of the blackbacked males would go with him. A new, small group would be formed. Although gorillas usually spend their entire lives with the same group, once in a while one or more will leave with a loner who

Male gorilla. This silverback is a lowland gorilla (Gorilla g. gorilla) *and differs only slightly from his mountain brother* (Gorilla g. beringei), *mainly in the size of the crest on his head. The mountain gorilla's is a bit larger.*

joins the group briefly. This is one way gorillas enlarge their range. Groups stay within their home ranges—areas of about eight to fifteen square miles—but the lone silver backs move much farther afield, and when other gorillas join them, they must leave the home territory.

By five o'clock, the sun was low in the western sky, casting the hagenia tree's shadow across the clearing and into the grass at the far edge. Kinguti rose from his feeding. He stood, stiff-legged, facing in the direction he wanted to go, and gave a series of low-pitched grunts. It was his signal to his group and meant, "Here I am; follow me." Without a backward glance he walked across the clearing and into the grass at its upper border. The other gorillas followed him. A two-year-old, fearing it had been forgotten, whined softly, and its mother returned to its side. The youngster grabbed her hair and pulled himself onto her back. The mothers with newborn infants held their babies to their breasts and walked three-legged to the spot where Kinguti had disappeared. The young males and the silverbacks, including the loner, trailed along behind. Only the old, cripped female lay still, too feeble to rise. The others ignored her as one by one they moved slowly from the clearing.

Kinguti walked about two hundred feet into the forest, found a spot to his liking, and began building a nest. This was where the group would spend the night. They had moved about a thousand feet during the day, from the time they had awakened in the morning, wandered to the clearing, and finally filed into this nesting spot. It was the normal movement of the group for any one day. Although they were nomads, seldom sleeping in the same place for two consecutive nights, the gorillas were far less active than other species of great apes.

Kinguti built his nest on the ground, for unlike the other species of apes, adult gorillas rarely nest in trees. He found a rotting log, sat against it and pulled handfuls of grass, twigs, and vines around him. He piled and patted them around his body, not weaving or binding them in any way. Concentrating on the nest's rim, he built a sizable mound of vegetation that finally surrounded him and butted against the log. When he was finished, the rim was two feet high, but the ground on which he would sleep hadn't been padded at all. Around him, the other gorillas were building their nests. One of the blackbacked males climbed ten feet into a tree and made a nest of branches and small twigs. He reached out, pulled in the branches, sometimes by merely bending them, but more often by breaking them off, and when his nest was finished it had a soft, comfortable base, unlike the ground nests of the other members of the group. However, his tree-nesting days were numbered, for as he grew still larger and heavier, he would have more and more trouble finding trees that could support him, and he would finally sleep on the ground and spend almost all his waking hours there.

One of the two-year-olds built a tiny nest beside his

mother, then abandoned it and climbed in with her. It would be at least another year before he slept by himself all the time.

No one knows exactly why gorillas build nests. Because most of them are on the ground, they offer no real protection from the rain, wind, and freezing temperatures which are common among the Virunga volcanoes. When the nests are built on hillsides, perhaps they help to brace the sleeping gorillas and keep them from rolling downhill during the night. The most likely reason for nestbuilding is that it is an activity left over from the time, tens of thousands of years ago, when gorillas lived in trees. The nests were useful there. Today, they probably represent the same kind of instinctual activity that a house dog goes through as he turns round and round on the living room carpet before curling up to sleep, much as his forest ancestors did thousands of years ago.

When darkness came, the gorillas were settled in their nests for the night. Far across the mountain, a member of Splitlip's group roared. Kinguti answered. Another roar, a few satisfied grunts, then silence fell on the group. The gorillas were asleep.

In the clearing surrounding the hagenia tree, the old female gorilla lay on the ground. The day's chilly rain had further weakened her and made her arthritis more painful. She coughed, tried to rise, fell back, then folded an arm under her head and lay on it.

A full moon rose in the east, silhouetting the hagenia

tree against the dark forest beyond. The bamboo growing on the clearing's lower border caught the moonlight and gleamed like a field of silver spears planted butt-first in the earth. The shadows grew inky black and as the night's dew fell, the grass sparkled in the moonlight.

A duiker stepped timidly from the trees that bordered the clearing. As it passed from the deep shadows of the forest, the moonlight caught its red coat, turning it to the color of burnt gold. The tiny antelope stopped at the clearing's edge, tested the night for danger, then walked daintily past the old gorilla and began feeding on herbs. It was a nighttime animal, unequipped to defend itself in daylight, and even in the safety of darkness relied on its speed for protection. It was also one of the favorite foods of leopards.

Even as the duiker fed, one of the cats sat watching it from the limb of a tree. The leopard had followed the antelope for almost a mile, waiting for a chance to pounce on it. Now, with its prey unaware of the danger behind it, the leopard prepared to charge. Its green eyes gleamed and it dug its claws deeper into the tree's bark preparing for the attack. It leaped to the ground and dashed into the clearing after the duiker. But at the first rattle of snapping twigs, the antelope bolted toward the far edge of the clearing and dived into the grass. In a flash it was gone.

The leopard stopped its charge, knowing from experience that a chase was useless in the dark forest. As it turned to retreat back into the forest, it heard a sound. The female gorilla had coughed. The cat stopped, studied her, then inched forward.

Leopards normally do not attack grown gorillas; they are too big and powerful. But now and then, they will seize a young one if it wanders away from its mother, or will take an old or diseased animal. The female lying in the clearing was old and ill, unable even to move, and the leopard was very hungry. It slowly circled the gorilla and, sensing her inability to hurt him, dashed forward and with its powerful jaws killed her. Then, unable to drag the three-hundred-pound carcass into a tree, where it normally took its prey, the cat crouched beside the dead gorilla and began eating.

By dawn, the leopard had gorged itself and moved into the forest to spend the day sleeping on a tree branch. A horde of ants and flies were attacking the dead gorilla. In a few days, only its bare skeleton would be left, for in the jungle, anything edible is soon eaten.

The flat, colorless light that precedes the sun lay lightly on the clearing. A ground mist hung a few inches above the grass. The snow fields atop Mount Karisimbi, one of the Virunga volcanoes, gleamed pink in the sky, and slowly the color crept down the slope and into the clearing. The day lightened. Suddenly, in an eye-wink of time, the sun popped above the forest, and in a matter of minutes the clearing lay warm and steaming. A beam of sunlight pierced the canopy of the hagenia tree, attracting the insects that had clung, cold and seemingly lifeless, to the trunk all night. A touraco flew into the clearing and landed on a moss-covered branch of the hagenia. It began preening its feathers. An insect fluttered through the beam of sunlight, looking like a silver jewel. The light exploded in a burst of red and green as the touraco swooped down from its branch, scooped up the insect, and returned to its perch. Another day had begun.

CHAPTER 4

Pongo

ONE MID-MORNING IN AUGUST, Pongo the orangutan moved slowly through the middle gallery of trees growing in Borneo's rain forest. Above her, the topmost layer interlaced its branches one hundred fifty feet in the air, making an unbroken canopy of leaves that shaded the forest's interior. The floor below was a swamp, a shallow, silt-laden body of water flowing slowly northward to the sea and carrying on its surface the rotting leaves and other vegetation dropped by the forest. The air was soggy, saturated with water vapor, for although August was the middle of the "dry season," there really was no *true* dry time in the forest. More than one hundred sixty inches of rain fell each year, and August was dry only to the extent that less rain fell then than in the "wet season," which began in October.

The woods through which Pongo moved was part of the enormous rain forest that covers three-quarters of the

Orangutan (Pongo pygmaeus) *and her baby.*

island of Borneo, from the Indonesian section, called
Kalimantan in the south, to the three small states, Sarawak,
Brunei and Sabah, in the north. Pongo lived in Sarawak, on
the low, flat coastal plain that stretches from the China
Sea southward to the foothills of the mountains that
straddle the earth's equator. Several rivers flow from
the mountains to the sea, and between two of them, in a
sixteen-hundred square mile area, Pongo lived her slow,
careful life.

She was twelve years old, a mature female. Her most
conspicuous feature was the coat of straggly, red hair that
grew on most of her body, except for her face, the palms of
her hands, and the soles of her feet, and which made her
look like an unkempt shag rug. She weighed about eighty-
five pounds, the average weight of a female, but much
lighter than an adult male, who might weigh more than two
hundred pounds. Pongo had tiny, human-like ears, a bulg-
ing snout, and thin lips. Her forehead was high, without
the heavy, overhanging brows and sagittal crest that mark
gorillas. Two cheek pads framed her face on either side
making it appear much broader than it actually was. These
pads, made up of fatty tissue, are common in adult orangs
and are especially noticeable in males. Their function, if any,
is unknown.

When Pongo stood erect, she was more than five feet
tall, and her arms hung almost to her ankles. But she seldom stood, for like all apes she was primarily a quadruped,

Young orangutan. Because its mother lives a solitary life, the young orangutan must play by itself unless there is a younger brother or sister present.

moving on four legs even in the trees. On heavy branches, she might stand and walk erect for a short distance, balancing herself by holding onto branches overhead. Or she might swing along, hand over hand, beneath a branch, a method of moving called brachiating. Except when brachiating, she always grasped the branches with at least three of her four limbs. She was truly an arboreal ape, spending practically all her time in the trees, yet she was very cautious and slow in her movements, almost as though she were afraid of falling. And this was understandable. Next to gorillas, orangutans are the largest apes, almost too large to be tree dwellers.

Pongo had had two babies since mating at the age of eight years, and the youngsters still lived and travelled with her. The older was a bright-eyed, playful three-year-old who constantly investigated the surrounding forest as he moved along with his mother. Unlike her, he was carefree, even wild in his movements, swinging, jumping and climbing madly up and down as he played. He used his feet as a second pair of hands, and although he never fell or lost his balance, now and then he found himself in insecure places. Then he whined for his mother, and she came as close as her great weight allowed, to help him retreat to safety.

Pongo's other youngster was a six-month-old female who spent its time either sleeping or nursing. It clung tightly to Pongo as she moved through the forest, and loosened its hold only when she stopped to feed. Then it crawled over her body, its eyes bright with curiosity. But as soon as Pongo moved, the baby screamed and dashed back to the shelter of her chest. Usually it clung with its face buried in her hair, but when the day was especially hot and oppressive it might turn around and cool itself by hanging on with its back pressed against her chest. At the first sign of danger or insecurity, however, it whirled around and clung to her, face-to-chest again.

Pongo had spent the night with her babies in a nest hung fifty feet above the forest's floor. It was a crude nest, merely a six-foot-wide platform woven from branches and twigs which Pongo had gathered and assembled into her night's home in about five minutes. Although the night was miserable with wind-driven rain lashing at the trees, she had remained on her soggy bed, curled up with the babies snuggled in the warmth of her huge body. The nest would last at least six months before it rotted in the tropical air, and the orangutan might return to it once or twice in her travels through the forest. More likely than not, however, it would stay abandoned after its brief use, for Pongo was a wanderer, seldom staying in the same nest for more than one or two nights. The main exception was when her babies were very young. Then she, like all orangutan mothers, might stay in the same nest for days at a time, leaving it only to feed, because the babies were too delicate to travel.

This morning, Pongo had awakened cold and wet when the sun cleared the eastern edge of the forest. As the nighttime chill left the forest, the orangutan turned over in her nest, stretched, rubbed her eyes with the back of her hands, yawned and stretched again. She scratched her back and stomach, then flopped back into the nest to nap again for several minutes. The three-year-old climbed out and fed on small, olive-sized fruits, spitting out the seeds, which spattered like rain on the leaves below. Pongo hauled herself upright with the "handle" branch which she had left hanging over the nest when making it the night before. With the infant clinging to her breast, she left the nest and joined her other youngster. After eating for a few minutes, she moved slowly but steadily through the jungle with the three-year-old male trailing behind. Unlike other mornings when her meanderings seemed aimless, Pongo moved in a direct line, as though sure of where she was going.

By mid-morning she had reached her destination, a clump of seventy-foot-tall trees growing deep in the forest. On each of the trees, just becoming ripe, hung the orangutans' favorite food, the coconut-sized durian fruit. Three other orangutans, a male, a female, and a year-old infant, already were in the trees feeding on the fruit. When Pongo and her youngsters arrived, the others looked up, then immediately returned to their feeding. Pongo settled onto a branch loaded with ripe fruit and began eating.

With one hand, she tore away the hard-shelled

Adult male orangutan. We do not know what purpose, if any, the large cheek pads serve.

durian from its twig, and although the husk was protected by a series of spiny projections, the orangutan seemed unconcerned about the sharp points. Having plucked a fruit, she held it in her hand and stripped away the tough outer covering with her mouth. Inside, the fruit contained a soft, cream-colored pulp and about ten chestnut-sized seeds. These seeds were what Pongo and the other orangutans were after. After spitting out the skin and pulp, they gobbled down the seeds. Unlike most apes, they were very clean eaters, taking care not to waste a bit of their delicacy.

While they were feeding, another orangutan, a lone male, came from the forest and joined them in the durian trees. He was ignored as completely as Pongo and her babies had been. There was very little social contact between the three hundred fifty orangutans who lived in that section of the forest. These apes lived alone, or in very small groups of two or three animals. Sometimes juveniles who were too old to remain with their mothers and too young to live the solitary lives of adults lived together for a year or so. In about two years, Pongo's three-year-old would drift away and join one of these adolescent groups. But by the time he was seven or eight, he would be living alone or with a female. Even then he would not form a family as such. He would merely mate, then go his solitary way.

The orangutans often saw each other in the forest, for they were constantly moving through the area bounded by the two rivers and the sea. But even if they nested in neighboring trees, or fed in the same one, as during the durian season, they paid little attention to each other. They did not call back and forth or greet each other as chimpanzees did. Nor did they drum on trees or beat their chests. They were the quietest and most solitary of all the apes. And, because of this, they were also the least known to men.

Wild orangutans are found in only two places in the world—Borneo and the northern tip of the island of Sumatra. Although most live in low-lying, swampy forests, some are found in the mountains, at elevations of three thousand feet. The people of Samatra gave them their commonly accepted name—orangutan—which means "old man of the forest." In Borneo, they are called *maias*.

Men and the orangutan, or *maias*, have lived together for many years on Sumatra and Borneo. Recent archeological digs in a northern Borneo cave at Niah uncovered both human and ape bones lying together in the dust. Judging from marks on the apes' bones, early man killed and ate the huge creatures thirty-five thousand years ago.

This early meeting seems to have set the stage for man's relationship with orangutans. For the most part, it has been the meeting of hunter and hunted. The Sea Dyaks, one of Borneo's native people, revere the *maias*, but that doesn't prevent them from killing the creatures. In fact, according to the Sea Dyaks, especially the older ones,

it is very good luck to have the skull of a *maias* hanging
from the rafters of one's house. The skull is assumed to represent an ancestral spirit hero, one who will watch over
the house and the people who live there. Also, certain of
the people believe that eating *maias* meat bestows part of
the ape's courage and power onto the man who eats it.
And there is still another reason why men shoot and kill the
slow, quiet orangutans. To collect specimens for zoos they
must kill the parents to capture the young.

By noon, the orangutans in the durian trees had
eaten their fill. The solitary male moved alone back into
the forest. Pongo sat high in the limbs of one of the trees,
nibbling at the durian seeds. Her three-year-old son sat next
to her, occasionally reaching across to take a bit of fruit
from her hands or mouth. The infant slept at her breast. In
the neighboring tree, the other female with her one-year-old
baby was making a daytime sleeping nest. She bent six or
seven branches under her until they were crushed by her
weight. Then she padded the platform with smaller
branches, twigs, and leaves which she tore away from the
nearby limbs. The entire process took only a couple of minutes, and although the nest was not so elaborate as the one
normally made for nighttime sleeping, it was large enough
for her and her baby, and comfortable enough for two or
three hours of midday napping.

The male orangutan who travelled with her made a
crude nest nearby. Within minutes, both animals were

curled up, ready for sleep. The one-year-old played near
the edge of his mother's nest, running along branches, hanging by one hand, and twirling slowly, pulling himself back
onto the branch to run and slide again. Pongo worked her
way to the edge of the durian tree, where branches from
another tree overlapped it. She slowly reached out,
dragged in several small branches and used them to pull in
a larger branch. Very carefully, she tested the branch with
her weight. Finally, satisfied that it would support her,
she released her hold on the durian branch and moved into
the other tree. Her three-year-old trailed along behind.
Moving steadily, the family passed from the durian grove
and into the forest where they would nap.

As she climbed into the tree where she planned to
sleep, Pongo heard human voices in the swamp below. She
peered through the thick foliage, for like all orangutans she
was curious about everything around her.

The men were foresters, moving through the swamp
to locate trees to be cut into lumber. When they were under
the durian trees, they saw the nests which the female and
male orangutans had made and in which they were now
sleeping.

"*Maias* nests," one of the men said, pointing.

"But I see no *maias*," his friend answered.

"Perhaps the nests are old."

"No, the leaves are still fresh."

At that moment, the one-year-old baby stuck its
head over a branch, curious about the men's voices.

"Ahh!" the men sighed together. Here was a prize! A baby *maias* was a year's wages on the seacoast.

"We must capture the baby," one man said. "I wonder where the mother is?"

He began to climb the tree. When the baby saw this, it screamed in panic and dashed toward its mother's nest. The mother awoke and poked her head over the edge of the nest. The male stood in his nest. Seeing the two adults, the man slid back down the tree.

"Now, it will be harder," he said to his friend. "Get the gun."

"This is illegal. We could go to jail," the other man said.

"I know," his friend answered. "But the Chinese trader on the seacoast offers much money for baby *maias*. Think of our families. Get the gun."

The man hurried away. The other stayed under the trees to watch the orangutans.

The male climbed from his nest and stood erect on a large branch above the man. The sight of the human angered him, for he had had contact with men before as they moved through the forest, cutting the trees. Annoyed, he gave out a series of sounds. GLUG-GLUG-GLUG, as though he were gulping water. He kissed the knuckles of one hand—SMACK! SMACK! He burped, a loud, two-toned sound that started on a low note and ended much higher. He repeated the sounds several times—SMACK, GLUG, BURP—seeming to work himself into greater anger. Then he began throwing branches. He stood on a large branch and tore away the twigs growing on it. Some he merely dropped to the ground, and others he swung away from him in the direction of the man standing below. He wrenched still larger branches from the tree, some of them up to three inches in diameter and ten feet long. These he lifted to his chest or over his head and threw with all his might. The man jumped nimbly from side to side to avoid being hit. Finally, the orangutan stretched as far erect as possible, and dived out at the man, but without letting go of the branch with his feet. His body swung around the branch and the ape ended hanging upside down by his feet, still threatening with his lips—SMACK, SMACK, BURP! The sounds were loud and strange enough to frighten other animals which the orangutan might meet from time to time in the forest—elephants, wild pigs, and deer. But the orangutan's threats made no impression on the man, a Sea Dyak, who had lived all his life at the edge of the forest and who knew the ways of the *maias*. He simply stood at the foot of the tree, watching the animals above him and ducking the branches that rained down. The large male, seeing that his threats made no impression, climbed higher into the tree, moved to another, and finally disappeared. The man stood fast, for he and his friend were not interested in adult orangutans. They wanted babies.

The second man returned with a shotgun. The female orangutan had left her nest and was sitting high in the tree. Her baby crouched near her. Both apes watched as the man climbed the tree next to the one in which they sat. When the man with the shotgun was level with the apes, he raised the gun and fired at the big female. She gasped, lost her balance for a moment, then painfully climbed back onto the branch and moved along it toward her nest. As she was climbing over the nest's edge, the man fired again, mortally wounding her. She fell into the nest, where she lay moaning. Her baby, frightened by the shots, screamed in fear and dashed to the nest, where he clung to his dying mother. The two men waited in their tree.

"Now?" one asked.

"A bit longer," his friend answered. He knew that orangutans, usually very shy and wanting nothing more than to be left alone, became extremely dangerous when cornered or wounded, or when their babies were in danger.

A few minutes later, the men slid to the ground and climbed the tree containing the nest. Very carefully, they looked over the edge. The female lay dead, sprawled on her back. The whimpering baby clung to her. One of the men pulled the baby free from its mother's body, and holding it tightly to him with one arm, climbed from the tree. The men moved fast now, for the killing or capturing of orangs in Sarawak was against the law, and there would be severe penalties if they were caught near the dead female or with the baby. They hurried to their boat, tied up at the edge of the river. They pushed the frightened baby into a

basket and covered it with a blanket. Then they paddled
toward their home village.

Later that week they took the little ape to the seacoast where an animal dealer lived, and sold it to him. By
now, deprived of its mother, and fed only boiled rice, the
baby had fallen ill. It had a cold, for like all apes it was
very susceptible to human disease, especially colds. It was
put into a small, dirty cage where two other baby orangutans huddled together. For two weeks it clung to the others.
Then, first one and then the other of the babies died,
leaving only the terrified one-year-old. The animal dealer
wandered along the waterfront day after day, trying to
find someone to buy his illegal orangutan, but no one appeared. The sale of babies had fallen off drastically since
reputable zoos of the world had agreed to buy no more
orangutans because of their rarity. There were some, not so
honest, that would pay up to five thousand dollars for each
baby smuggled out of Borneo or Sumatra. But no buyer
showed up for the one living in the back room of the
dealer's house. However, word about the baby orangutan
leaked out, and three weeks after being captured, the little
ape was rescued by a game warden. The warden swooped
down on the dealer one night, took the baby away and
jailed the dealer. The orangutan was taken to the Sarawak
Museum, where the curator and his wife cared for the few
orphans rescued from smugglers. The new baby was cured
of its illness, and when it was about two years old it was

Infant orangutan. As it grows older, its head will change shape. The snout will push forward and the forehead recede.

released in a national park, where, maybe, it could live a life free from human interference.

Man is the orangutan's only enemy. Because the apes move so slowly through the trees, a man can easily trail them on the ground until he can get a clear shot. There was a time, shortly after Europeans came to Borneo and Sumatra, when shooting orangutans was considered a great sport. One "sportsman" bragged about killing three in one day. During the nineteenth century, hundreds of the great apes were killed, some for sport, many as specimens for museums. An American collector killed forty-three during one trip to Borneo. Because it was almost impossible to capture adult animals, mothers were killed so that their babies could be taken. Unfortunately, that did not end the orangutans' suffering, for many of the captured infants never lived to see the inside of a zoo. They died of mistreatment, disease, or simply loneliness. Even today, for each orangutan one sees in a zoo, usually five or six other animals have died from shooting, disease, or starvation.

No species can withstand such slaughter, and the orangutans' numbers have fallen to the danger point. In some areas of Sarawak, for instance, where many *maias* lived one hundred years ago, today not one is left. The entire *maias* population in Sarawak is about seven hundred animals, and the world's wild population, living in Borneo and Sumatra, is no more than five thousand.

During the episode in the durian grove, Pongo and her two offspring were able to slip away unnoticed. At the first blast from the shotgun, they moved farther into the forest, pausing each hundred yards or so to look back out of curiosity. Eventually they travelled far away from the grove, deeper into the jungle. As the fright brought on by the gun left them, they slowed their movements and nibbled on leaves and fruits. They discovered a hollow tree filled with bees. Pongo opened the nest with a stick, then she and her three-year-old gorged themselves on the honey inside. Afterwards, as they moved along a branch, the young male came upon a deadly green tree snake, lying stretched in the sun. The sight so startled the little ape that he lost his balance and fell several feet before catching another branch. He often saw snakes as he climbed through the trees, and usually just moved aside. But his reaction when coming on one unexpectedly was much the same as that of a human under similar circumstances—he was startled.

An hour after leaving the durian grove, Pongo stopped and built a crude daytime nest. She curled into it with her two babies and slept most of the afternoon. By four o'clock she was awake and eating once more. As Pongo fed, she came to a fork of two branches where a small pool of water had collected. She dipped a hand into the water, held it over her head, and drank the water that ran from it. She kept dipping a hand and holding it aloft until her thirst was quenched. She found and ate a column of tree ants; a bird's nest caught her attention, and after eating the eggs it contained she sat watching the three-year-old tear it apart. Then, before stopping for the night, Pongo heard a sound which was becoming all too familiar in the forest— a chain saw.

Lumbering was an important industry, probably the single most important, in the area in which Pongo lived.

Several species of fine hardwoods grew there in the swampy lowlands, and with increasing frequency the trees were found, marked, and cut. The area was a forest reserve set aside by the government as a permanent forest where cutting did not exceed the ability of the trees to replenish themselves. But by cutting, even on this selective basis, the forests are opened, making them unsuitable for orangutans, who need thick growths in which to live. For the past hundred years or so, lumbering has been added to the shotgun as an agent responsible for pushing the *maias* ever closer to extinction. As the forests are cut, the apes move farther inland, but eventually they will run out of places to go.

At the sound of the chain saw, Pongo turned aside and led her son southward in the general direction of the mountains. This was not the first time she had been forced to leave a section of the forest. Each two or three years brought the saws farther into the virgin growths, and each time they came, Pongo moved southward. She was twelve years old, and unless man prevented her living out her natural life expectancy, she would last for perhaps another twenty. But by then there probably would be little if any forest left for her and her offspring.

In fact, unless something positive is done very soon, there will be no wild orangutans by the turn of the twenty-first century. All that will be left will be a few zoo animals, some well-treated, others poorly cared for, all bored, and most neurotic from confinement. Thus far, the captive animals have not bred well enough to replace themselves. A large sanctuary is needed, some place in the orangutans' natural homeland where the creatures can live freely and safely among the trees, and where they can be studied. But, as of 1967, there was no such place and no definite plans to establish one. So, possibly, Pongo was one of the last of her kind—a wild, free-living orangutan.

Shortly before sundown, she built a nest for the night. It was high in a tree that stood miles away from the nearest chain saw or shotgun. The forest round about was quiet, damp, and gloomy, still untouched by humans. A family of proboscis monkeys swung into the nesting tree, saw the great apes and noisily moved on. These red-haired

SAN DIEGO ZOO

Proboscis monkey (Nasalis larvatus). This average-sized monkey is found only on the island of Borneo. As the male ages, his nose becomes even larger.

monkeys with the ridiculously long noses lived only on Borneo, alongside the orangutans in the wet forests, and the two species encountered each other frequently. A wild pig splashed through the water at the foot of the tree. Far away, an elephant trumpeted. By the time Pongo finished her nest, the sun was a red blob lying on the western horizon. The orangutan climbed into her nest and nursed her infant. The three-year-old male played alone on a nearby branch. Then as the sky darkened, he bounced into the nest and curled up beside his mother. Pongo turned on her side; she scratched an itchy place on her belly; she rolled to her back, pulled in a leaf that grew above the nest, ate it, and then fell asleep.

CHAPTER 5

Lar

AT DAYBREAK, Lar the gibbon awoke in his sleeping-tree high on the slopes of Doi Dao, a mountain in Thailand. He had spent the night sitting on a branch of the tree with his legs drawn up to his chest, his arms draped across his knees, and his head buried in the warm fur of his thighs. He raised his head, yawned, and stood to stretch his muscles.

Lar was a slender, straw-colored ape with white fur on his hands and feet and a ring of white fur around his dark brown face. The smallest of all anthropoids, he stood less than three feet tall and weighed only fifteen pounds. He had large, black eyes and a thin nose with nostrils that opened downward, like a man's, instead of forward, as in other apes. His arms, with their thin, hooklike hands, were extremely long, proportionally much longer than those of any other primate. They spanned almost five feet, and on

Adult gibbon (Hylobate
lar).

the rare occasions when Lar trailed them as he walked upright, they hung below his ankles.

After considerable stretching and yawning, Lar
glanced at the forest around him. It lay still and cool, the
heat of day many hours away. A stream flowed among
bushes that crowded each other on the forest floor, a mere
trickle now in January, the dry season. A heavy dew had
fallen during the night, and the tree trunks stood wet and
black, barely visible as they soared upward to the dark mass
of the canopy overhead.

Lar glanced up at the branch where the rest of his
family still slept—his father, mother, and two-year-old
sister—all huddled together, their backs matted and wet
from the dew. A new baby slept warm and dry, buried in
the fur of its mother's belly. Unlike the chimpanzees, gorillas, and orangutans, the gibbons did not build sleeping
nests, but slept like monkeys on branches each night. And,
like the monkeys, they had thick pads of skin, called ischial
callosities, growing on their rumps. These pads, not needed
by nest-building apes, cushioned the little gibbons as they
sat on the bare branches.

Lar left his branch to join the rest of the family. He
had been the first baby, born when his mother was nine
years old, and for *most* of his eight years he had been a
close part of the family. Until the new baby was born eight
weeks ago, he had spent each night with his parents on
whatever branch they chose for sleeping. But because he

was eight years old and rapidly becoming an adult, his father had become increasingly irritable over the past months, lashing out at Lar, especially when he came close to his mother. Then, when the new baby came, even his mother had rejected him, so Lar slept slightly apart, no longer welcome. Yet Lar still was uncomfortable removed from the family he had known and lived with all his life. He stayed nearby at night, and during the day fed where he could see them. Each day the tension between him and his father became greater, and it was obvious that soon Lar must leave the family. But he was a very unwilling outcast.

As he moved to join them in the tree, he walked upright, using his arms to balance himself. He held them level with his shoulders, bent upward at the elbows with the wrists hanging loose. Usually, he preferred to swing along among the branches, and spent less than ten percent of his travelling time walking. But the branch was too large to hook his hands over, and since the distance to his family was short, he tripped along, dainty as a tightrope walker, on its upper surface. When he reached the tree trunk, he shinnied up to the branch where his family slept. His sister awoke with a squeal as he brushed by her, then, recognizing him, reached out to nip his ankle. They had played together for a year and a half, ever since she was six months old and large enough to leave her mother for short periods, chasing each other round and round through the trees, wrestling as they hung by an arm or leg, and sometimes tumbling into the bushes below. But as Lar approached adulthood, his bites became harder, making her squeal with pain. Then their father would race through the branches to attack him. Gradually, he played less with his sister, and actually tried to fight with her, sending her whimpering to her mother, who would embrace or groom her for a few minutes. But when Lar tried to get the same attention, his father dashed in, cuffing and biting as though jealous of him and seeing him as a rival for the mother's attentions.

So when his sister nipped him as an invitation to play, Lar ignored her and moved past the family toward a leafless vine that trailed down beside the sleeping branch. A few grapes were growing on the vine. Lar reached out and pulled the vine to him as he sat on the branch. Then, holding it with one foot, he plucked the grapes and popped them into his mouth. He chose them carefully, rejecting those that were spoiled, for like most gibbons, he was a dainty eater. He skinned and seeded the grapes with his lips, even biting away portions that were slightly overripe before swallowing the fruit.

While he ate, the rest of the family awoke. They stretched and yawned, and the baby began nursing. It was a tiny thing, which had weighed slightly more than one pound when it was born, and even now at eight weeks of age looked like an overgrown spider, with its scrawny legs and arms and tiny hair-covered body. It had slept the night buried in its mother's fur. When she awoke, it squirmed up to her breast, where it fastened onto a nipple. The mother sat while it fed, spending the time grooming her arms, delicately picking away the dirt, seeds, or insects she found. Probably because she, like most apes, spent so much of her time grooming herself and being groomed by others, her body was completely free of parasites and dirt, although she never bathed, for gibbons cannot swim and never enter water.

Lar's father moved to the grapevine. Squatting beside his son as though there were nothing wrong in their being so close, he plucked and ate a few of the fruits. So long as Lar didn't approach his mother too closely, his father tolerated him, although he no longer played with him as he had years before.

After a few minutes of feeding, and as the morning light filled the sleeping-tree, the father sat back on his branch and began calling out the loud, clear song of the gibbons. "WHOOP-WHOOP-WHOOP-WHOOP-WHOOP!" His call started slowly and on a low note, then became faster and faster as it rose to a high-pitched, piercing end. Over and over. "WHOOP-WHOOP-WHOOP!" It excited the rest of the family and everyone except the baby chimed in. Another family of gibbons farther down the mountain heard and picked it up. Then the family that lived across the stream added its voices. Then another and another. The calling rang back and forth through the forest, over and over. It was the gibbons' morning call, sung out each day, and probably was a signal that each family was awake and ready to defend its territory.

The wild chorus kept up for an hour. During that time, the gibbons didn't move or feed, but simply sat or swung in their trees, calling back and forth to each other. By the time the sun had risen, the calling was all over and the forest lay still again except for the birds, who were now awake and about their daily lives. Lar's mother stood up and, chattering noisily to the others, set off to find food.

First, she positioned the baby low on her belly and slightly to one side, raising the leg that was nearest the baby in order to support the infant. Then she ran along the branch, using her arms as crutches for the leg that propped up the baby. When she reached the trunk she climbed higher in the tree to the small branches that made up the canopy. Hooking her hands over a branch, she swung along it, hand over hand. When she reached its end, she leaped the ten feet or so that separated the branch from a branch in the next tree. With no interruption, she swung along under it until she came to the next space, which she easily jumped. Her movements were swift and sure, and she moved so quickly that she seemed to glide along under the branches. Her leaps were made with absolute accuracy, and as she propelled her body into space she thrust her head and arms forward, as though diving for the next handhold. This was her usual way of travelling. Gibbons are brachiators, swinging and leaping through the trees. This

probably accounts for their extremely long arms and hands and remarkable agility. Although the orangutans, chimpanzees, and, to a lesser degree, young gorillas, also brachiate, the gibbons are the masters of the trees. Their scientific name, *Hylobates*, means "tree dweller."

As Lar's mother moved away from the sleeping-tree, the other members of the family followed her with Lar trailing along behind.

The father, a sixteen-year-old in his prime, was an especially good acrobat. Because he was strong and not slowed as the mother was by a baby, he made spectacular leaps between trees, at times diving thirty feet or more into space before catching a new branch. Once, just as he was about to launch himself into the air, the twig from which he was hanging snapped. Instead of falling, the gibbon seemed to reverse himself in mid-air, grabbed the stub of the broken twig, swung completely around it, leaped, and caught the next branch, all without so much as a pause.

But that is not to say that the gibbons do not fall from time to time. One baby, born after Lar's two-year-old sister, had tumbled from a tree and had been killed. Lar himself had a badly knitted fracture in one arm from such a fall. Many gibbons are known to have broken bones from their wild flights through the jungle.

Lar and his family swung along for about three hun-

RICHARD PALMER

Gibbon brachiating. Gibbons are the most agile of all primates, often leaping more than twenty feet from tree to tree.

dred yards from the sleeping tree before catching up to the mother. Hanging by one hand in a light gray tree that stood sixty feet tall, she was eating the dark purple plums that grew in its green canopy. As she hung, twisting and turning, she gathered the fruit with either her free hand or one of her feet. Then she swung onto the top of the branch, sat, and while she held on with a foot or hand, carried the bitter plums to her mouth with the other hand. Lar's father and sister joined her. Lar sat apart and ate. Once, he swung too close to his mother for the father's liking and the male became tense and restless, opening and closing his mouth with much snapping of his teeth.

The gibbons were not the only occupants of the tree, for the plums were prized by the other primates who lived in the forest. Macaques and langur monkeys swarmed among the branches, each ignoring the other. The macaques sat hunched up, stuffing their mouths. The langurs scrambled through the tree, chattering and chasing each other. Both of these species had cheek pouches which they filled with plums to be taken away and eaten in quieter surroundings. The gibbons, not having cheek pouches, had to eat in the tree, close to the food supply.

After they had fed for half an hour, the gibbons were startled by a cry of alarm from Lar's sister—a loud, high-pitched shout. The family looked through the trees. They had excellent eyesight, the best among the primates, probably because they depended so much on their eyes in their wild brachiating. Long before a human could have seen the very old gibbon who approached, the family was aware of him. The mother reached out and scooped up the baby, who had been playing by itself among the leaves. She pressed it against her belly, where it grabbed her hair. The father swung toward the stranger, ready to defend the family territory; sister swung closer to her mother; Lar stayed uncertainly to one side.

The newcomer was an old male, well over thirty years of age. As he approached, his movements were relaxed and gentle, and his face was pulled into a smile with his tongue stuck out, the usual greeting of a gibbon who was friendly and meant no harm. When he entered the plum tree, the family recognized him. He was a relative, possibly the father of one of Lar's parents, who usually lived with the family. Why he had drifted away from the group was unknown, but it was obvious that he was happy to be back. He embraced Lar's father and squealed with happiness. He investigated the baby and groomed Lar's mother. And after the first few minutes, the old gibbon was ignored by the others. Gibbon families will accept very old males or females in their midst, probably because they pose no threat to the parents' relationships with each other. Families often travel about with a grandmother or grandfather as part of the group.

Their hunger satisfied after three hours in the plum tree, the gibbons followed Lar's father when he moved on.

He swung leisurely through the branches, his belly full and round. In one tree he found a line of ants streaming along the trunk and stopped to eat them. Placing the back of one hand against the tree, he let the ants climb aboard, then licked them off his hair. Lar discovered a bird's nest. He ate the eggs inside it, then tore the nest apart. If the nest had contained nestlings, Lar would have eaten them, for the birds, eggs, and insects that he ate rounded out his normal diet. His main food consisted of whatever kind of fruit was ripe, but although this was filling, Lar needed the protein supplied by meat or eggs.

A few hundred yards from the plum tree, Lar's father swung down into the bushes that grew along a little stream. Hanging by one hand, he satisfied his thirst by dipping his free hand into the stream and licking off the water. The family joined him. The old grandfather dropped to the ground and crouched beside the stream to drink, dipping his hand as the others had done. When they had drunk their fill, the gibbons jumped into the bushes and climbed back among the trees.

They moved leisurely, stopping frequently to investigate anything that might prove interesting to eat—seeds, fruit, leaves, and insects. By noon they reached a tree, much taller than the others, into which they climbed. High in the crown, they settled down for their daily rest. Lar's father lay on his side on a broad limb while the old male groomed him. The baby left its place on the mother's belly and swung among the twigs overhead. Once, it dropped onto the father, who rolled over and played with its feet and hands. But the baby was too active for him and he gently nudged it aside. Lar's sister came up and nipped it gently, then swung away, inviting it to play. The baby started after her, but its mother reached out and held it back. The sister looked over her shoulder, saw that the baby was not following, and returned to its side, where she sat playfully grappling with it. She nipped it a bit too hard and the baby cried. Immediately the father looked up and the mother gathered the infant to her body. The sister turned away, found a sunny branch, and went to sleep.

At the group's edge, Lar sat grooming himself. Then, as though bored, he moved toward the rest of the family. He swung over to his sister. When a couple of feet away from her, he sat on the branch and turned his back, an invitation to be groomed. She recognized the signal, came to him, and began picking through the hair on his back. After a few minutes, she stopped and turned *her* back, inviting Lar to groom her.

As the gibbons rested in their tree, they presented a picture of contentment—father, mother, three youngsters, and grandfather. Because they had lived together for so long, each animal knew his place. There seldom was any physical fighting, and so long as the youngsters were immature, they were loved and protected. The family was a very closely knit group and the only outsiders allowed were those who were old and those who were being forced out, such as Lar. Even with him, the father usually held back from outright physical violence, limiting his attacks to noise and chases. So long as Lar did not come too close to his mother, he was safe. But because he was close to being fully grown, he no longer was truly a part of the family. He must leave very soon.

His chance came later that day. After resting until mid-afternoon, the family moved off to find more food. As they approached a favorite food tree, located on the edge of their territory, they heard gibbon alarm cries coming from it. They raced madly through the branches. When they came to the tree, they saw another family of gibbons swinging and leaping among its branches. It was a large family—father and mother, four youngsters, and two old animals. A leopard had climbed into the tree and captured one of the old animals while the gibbons were resting. It held its victim between its jaws. The other apes circled, crying and trying to make the cat drop its prey. The male gibbon was the most aggressive, swinging to within inches of the cat's claws and screaming madly. Lar's father raced ahead to join the attack, and soon both families were harassing the leopard. The cat retreated down the tree and leaped to the ground, still holding the old gibbon in its mouth. The leopard was one of the gibbons' few enemies. Occasionally it took one of the apes, but usually it caught only the very young or very old. The big pythons which lived among the trees also caught an ape once in a while, but for the most part, agile, healthy gibbons had little to fear except man.

The forests on the side of the mountain called Doi Dao were near several springs thought to be sacred by Buddhist natives. And because the Buddhists held all life as holy, they did not harm the gibbons. Other natives considered the gibbons good omens, and although they captured a few as pets, they did not kill any. But there were other natives who looked upon the little apes as food for their cooking pots. And they were the most dangerous of all the gibbons' enemies, for with their guns they killed many of the creatures.

As yet the gibbons are in no immediate danger of extinction. They are the most widespread of all apes, living from sea level to about seven thousand feet on the sides of southeastern Asia's mountains. They are found in the state of Assam in India, and in Burma, Thailand, all of Indochina, the Malay Peninsula, and on the islands that stretch southeasterly from the mainland. There are from five to eight species, depending upon what authority one listens to. One of these species has possibly been exterminated by the war in Viet Nam. There are two major types: *Hylobates*, of which Lar and his family were members, and *Symphalangus*, a much larger gibbon called a siamang whose main distinguishing feature is the sac on his throat. When he calls, he fills the sac with air and the resonating sound can be

Siamang (Symphalangus syndactylus) *and her baby.*

heard for miles. The siamang is black and lives only on the Malay Peninsula and the island of Sumatra. We don't know much about him other than where he lives, so we can only assume that his life might be much the same as that of *Hylobates*. Many of the *Hylobates* are also black. In fact, the big male whom Lar's father helped in the fight with the leopard was shiny black, as was one of his daughters, a seven-year-old who still lived with her family.

Having sent the leopard on its way, although with a victim, the gibbons turned to quarrelling among themselves. One would think that after fighting a common enemy, they would be the best of friends. Far from it. The family which had first sent out the cry of alarm was an invader into the territory belonging to Lar's family. The fruit tree stood just inside an imaginary line which over the years had been recognized as the boundary between the two territories. Lar and his family lived in an area that was about forty acres in size—roughly as large as nine square blocks in the city. The other family, having more members, claimed sixty acres as its territory. And while neither territory was defined by a line or river or break in the trees, the gibbons knew their property to within a few feet. There was no doubt about it. The black male's family had invaded the territory of Lar's family.

In gibbon society this was intolerable, and Lar's family set out to make it right. Led by the father, they swung wildly through the tree, made short charges among the invaders, then dashed back screaming. When this failed to move the other family, Lar's group stood on the heavier branches and growled. Their heads were thrown back, their arms were held level with their shoulders and their hands and heads shook violently.

Recognizing this as extreme anger, the second family withdrew from the tree. And as they did, Lar's group quieted. They had done what they had set out to do—drive invaders from their property. Their rage had been immediate, but there had been no violence, for gibbons rarely fight. Even a larger group would finally respect the territorial rights of a smaller, and this is what the black male's family did.

Once out of the fruit tree, they were in their own territory, and here they ceased retreating. They turned and began calling back to the other gibbons. Gradually, the anger on both sides faded, and the two families sat or swung in their respective trees, feeding. Lar, who had been as vocal and angry as the rest of his family, drifted away from the family's center and toward the other group. The sleek, black female had caught his eye. He moved far out to the edge of the fruit tree and watched her. She too, stayed on the edge of her family, for she was at the age when her mother looked upon her as a rival. Whereas Lar's father made the young male keep his distance from the mother by hoots and cries, the black female's mother was not above hurting her daughter. In gibbon families, as among many animals, jealousy and fighting among females is more common than among males. In fact, the males often must stop the squabbles in order to keep peace in the family.

Lar swung from his tree to the branch where the little female gibbon sat grooming herself. As he approached, he gave the friendly greeting sign—a smile with tongue stuck out, and a relaxed, slow approach. The female did not move. When he was close to her, he reached out and embraced her, then presented his back for grooming. She picked at his hair a few times, then turned her back. At that moment, her father jumped down on the couple and before Lar could retreat to his tree, he was bitten on the ear for intruding into the black gibbon's territory. He squealed in pain and dashed back home. The female swung away screaming, chased by her father. As they disappeared into the forest, the rest of their family swung away after them, leaving the border between the two territories to Lar and and his group.

By five o'clock in the afternoon the sun was well down in the western sky and the gibbons were moving away from the fruit tree, their afternoon feeding finished. The father led them deep into their territory, toward a sleeping-tree where they would spend the night. Usually, these trees were well away from territorial borders, and were used for several consecutive nights. There might be a dozen such trees in each family's home territory, chosen for the protection they gave from wind and rain. During the course of a year, the apes would visit each one several times, depending on which fruit was ripe.

Lar's father moved rapidly; there was no dawdling, for the day was nearing its end and there was only one reason for the trip—to reach the sleeping-tree. Within minutes, the family scrambled into it and onto their favorite branch. They called a few times and were answered by other groups in the forest. Then they settled down for the night. It had been an average day's travel for them, less than one-half mile.

Lar, his ear sore from the bite of the black male, tried to move in next to his mother. But his father swung down and drove him away. Sitting on a branch a few feet away from the family, Lar cried fretfully in the way that a few years before would have brought his mother to his side. But she was busy nursing the baby and ignored him. He moved closer to his sister, but she remembered the sharpness of his teeth and swung over to her father's side. Lar next tried the ancient grandfather, but he too rejected him. The young gibbon swung away. He looked back at his family snuggled together on their sleeping-branch. He was completely outside. Slowly he left the tree and headed for the spot where he had seen the black female that afternoon.

All that night he sat in the fruit tree on the territory's border. In the morning, when the gibbons in the forest around him whooped their calls, he joined in. Within

minutes the black female showed up in the next tree and
Lar leaped across the space that separated them. This
time there was no father to interrupt their courtship and
she accepted him as her mate.

Now they were alone. Neither of their families
would accept them in their territories, so the two gibbons
travelled through the forest, swinging rapidly among the
upper branches looking for a place of their own. They
dashed for safety when they encountered another family
into whose homeland they blundered, or they sat quietly
until the danger had passed them by. At length, they came
to an old clearing carved from the forest by native farmers.
Carefully, they worked their way around it and into a
clump of bamboo on the far side. There they fed, eating
the tender upper ends of the stalks and munching on young
leaves. They moved on, found water in tiny cups formed
by the crotches of trees, drank, and moved still deeper into
this new, unknown forest. Finally, they came to a mountain called Doi Intanon by the Thai people. Part way up its
slopes they found a lovely valley where bear, barking deer,
and the wild, hump-backed cattle called gaur roamed
among the trees, open grasslands, and low-lying knolls.
But they did not see or hear other gibbons. So they stopped
travelling. They found plums and fig trees which, in season,
would bear the juicy, bitter fruit they loved. There was
bamoo, the greenish-rust colored fruit with tough skin and
seeds that were covered with fibrous meat. There were wild

mangoes and bamboo, nutmeg and grapes. There was everything needed to fill a gibbon's needs. The valley became their territory, much to the delight of the few people who lived there. The natives felt that good luck had come to them with the gibbons, for these were people who loved and revered the agile little apes. No one hunted them or tried to capture them as pets. Each morning, the valley rang with their calling, and seven months after they arrived, a new, whimpering voice was added. Lar and his mate had a tiny, straw-colored baby with spidery legs and arms. From that time on they were truly home, and outsiders no more.

CHAPTER 6

When Cousins Meet

AT THE ZOO IN San Diego, California, a mass of visitors crowded against the railing in front of the grotto where Trib the gorilla perched on a tree stump. The people pointed, laughed, and talked to each other about the young gorilla who sat quietly watching them. A few feet away, other zoo visitors peered at the orangutans and chimpanzees. And up the hill, another crowd enjoyed the antics of the gibbons as they swung and leaped in their bamboo jungle.

The San Diego Zoo has the world's largest collection of wild animals, some of them the rarest animals still living. Yet the several million people who visit the zoo each year spend far more time watching the apes than looking at the other rarities—the beautiful okapis, the almost extinct oryxes, the gentle nene geese, and dozens of others. Why?

The answer is that we humans are enormously interested in our cousins, the anthropoid apes. We are in-

Young gorilla at the San Diego Zoo.

trigued by their manlike features and their almost human manners. They entertain us much as circus clowns do. And perhaps because they look so human, yet are not, we feel superior to them, amused by what seems to us to be a mimicry of humanity.

For most of the time that men—especially white men —have known about the anthropoids, they have looked on the creatures as not quite animal, yet certainly not human. Most people, among them even a few early scientists, could not believe that the apes were simply other species of animals. In early Christian time they were assumed to be fallen souls, people whom the devil, Satan, had corrupted. In fact, for a time they were thought to be Satan himself disguised in almost human form, visiting earth in order to lure people into sinful ways.

In much earlier times monkeys were kept as pets by the kings and princes of western Asia. We read in the Bible that Solomon, King of Israel, kept them one thousand years before the time of Christ. Still earlier in Egypt, hamadryas baboons were considered sacred messengers of the great god Toth, and after living out their lives in the temples were mummified and buried. Today in Malayasia, gibbons are thought to be both good and evil spirits. If a gibbon leaps onto the roof of a house, that house eventually will burn down. If a Malayan dreams about a gibbon, the animal becomes his helper, a source of strength and inspiration. To the Sea Dyaks of Borneo the orangutan is a part of the family heritage and its skull is a sacred object called

Antu Gergasi, an ancestral, god-like being. In India, langur monkeys are fed by the people and allowed the freedom of temples and villages. They often become nuisances, destroying property, but official efforts to control them are met with heavy resistance from the people, who feel that the monkeys are sacred.

By the time of the Middle Ages in Europe, many nobles and other people of high rank kept primates as pets. They were cared for by the jesters, who used them as entertainment for the ladies and gentlemen of the court. Eventually, owning one became a mark of social position. After America was discovered, the New World primates, especially the tiny marmosets, became very popular. At one time the city of Paris imposed a tax on the importation of primate pets, and because there were so many coming through its gates, a large part of Paris' income came from this tax.

For the most part, however, man has dealt far less gently with his ape cousins. As we saw, in Borneo, prehistoric man hunted orangutans thirty-five thousand years ago to fill his cooking pots. In Africa, the natives have killed chimpanzees and gorillas for centuries, sometimes as part of religious ceremonies but more often simply to be cooked and eaten.

When the white men of Europe began exploring the world, the first apes they discovered were the chimpanzees and lowland gorillas in western Africa and the orangutans on the islands off Asia. These early travellers brought back

Golden marmosets (Leontideus rosalia). *These beautiful primates are found in the rain forests of Brazil. They are about the size of kittens.*

stories about the strange, manlike creatures of the jungle, stories that were part truth and part fantasy. One story, about lowland gorillas, whom the storyteller calls "monsters," reports that, "The people of the country, when they travel in the woods, make fires where they sleep at night, and in the morning, when they are gone, the *Pongoes* [gorillas] will come and sit about the fire, till it goes out." He goes on to write that the gorillas also ". . . fall upon elephants . . . and so beat them with their clubbed fists and pieces of wood, that they will run away roaring. . . ." His imagination soars to even greater heights as he writes that "When they [gorillas] die among themselves, they cover the dead with great heaps of boughs and wood, which are commonly found in the forest."

These fantasies did not stop with activities like beating up elephants or sitting around campfires. Perhaps because the apes were so manlike, yet so obviously not men, they were accused of terrible crimes against humanity. The most common charge against them was that they kidnapped young women to be their wives. This is absolute nonsense, of course, but it has persisted in one form or another up to present times. Many of the monsters in science fiction stories are apes of one kind or another. *King Kong*, a movie made in the 1930's, was about a giant gorilla who lived on an island and to whom the unfortunate natives had to sacrifice one of their young women each year. Kong met his fate when he abducted a white girl and in the dramatic finale of the movie was shot down from the Empire State

Building by airplanes. But the apes' supposed crimes did not end with kidnapping. Edgar Allen Poe, the American author, wrote a story, "Murder in the Rue Morgue," in which an orangutan slipped into an apartment and killed two women by slicing their throats with a razor, then stuffed one of the bodies up the chimney.

Maybe people want to believe these horror stories. Perhaps they want to think that real monsters live with them in the world. And certainly, at first glance, apes, especially the huge gorillas and orangutans, qualify as monsters. In any event, for several centuries very little was done to learn who the creatures truly were. Even some of the early scientists who travelled into the jungles searching for them were far more interested in getting specimens than in observing the beasts. "Getting specimens" is a polite way of saying that the animals were killed, and their bodies taken to museums to be stuffed and mounted. A certain amount of killing was necessary for scientists to study the animals' anatomy, to learn how they differed from each other and from man. But all too often, the killing became slaughter.

In addition to the scientific collectors, other hunters invaded the apes' homelands and killed them for sport. These "sportsmen" killed for fun. Fortunately, this type of "fun" is no longer practiced, at least against apes.

Soon after the western world discovered the strange, man-like primates, zoos demanded living animals for their exhibits, and a new type of hunter travelled into the jungles. He was a collector who took at least some of the apes alive. But the creatures did not walk willingly into traps; a way had to be devised to take them. An adult gorilla or orangutan was much too strong to be captured. So babies were the prime objects of the search. But as we have seen, ape babies stay close to their mothers, who in turn are quite protective of their offspring. So, before a baby could be captured, its mother had to be shot. And if other adult primates got in the way, they too were killed. Once the baby was captured, it was transported to the nearest port, where an animal dealer bought it and sold it to the zoos' representatives. We have seen how fragile these wild babies are. Most died before or shortly after they reached the zoos of Europe and America. One chimpanzee named Consul lasted only fifteen months in an English zoo in the late 1800's. (Incidentally, our ancient friend Proconsul, who started it all—men and apes—was named for the chimpanzee, Consul. His name, Proconsul, means "before Consul.")

Under the impact of hunters and collectors, the population of the world's apes began to drop. And the creatures' plight became worse as more native people moved to the edges of the jungles. They cut the trees, and farms appeared where formerly only tropical rain forests had been. As lumbering became an important industry, still more trees were cut. Herdsmen drove their cattle deep into the forests to graze. And the number of apes slipped closer to zero.

Finally, just a few years ago, scientists and conservationists realized that if we are going to have apes living any place but in a few zoos around the world, something must be done. The first need was to protect the animals from hunting and collecting. Today, all are protected by law, although this is difficult and often impossible to enforce. Next, we had to learn more about the life of wild primates. In the last few years, scientists have studied the apes where they live—the tropical rain forests.

Now, with more knowledge about apes' lives and a conviction that we must save the remnants of their populations, perhaps there is hope that they will not disappear. But it is a slim hope. Orangutans are still killed and their babies smuggled out of Borneo; cattle still graze ever deeper in the forests where gorillas and chimpanzees forage for food; warfare still destroys much of the homeland of the gibbons. Some authorities believe that the orangutan will be extinct by the end of this century; that the mountain gorilla, if he is lucky, might last into the next century; that the lowland gorilla also is in grave danger; that the chimpanzee might survive another one hundred years; and that by the end of the twenty-first century, a mere one hundred and fifty years from now, the gibbon will become extinct. All that will be left will be a few zoo animals scattered around the world. But there is very little hope here, for these captives will be far too few to maintain the population, and captive apes, especially orangutans and gorillas, breed poorly in captivity. As of 1967, there were about two hundred and eighty orangutans in

zoos, about one hundred and twenty lowland gorillas, perhaps twelve mountain gorillas, and a few thousand chimpanzees and gibbons. These might be among the last of
their kind. By the time that your children are grown, there
is a very good chance that they will never see a living ape.

Why should we save them? After all, nature chooses
its strongest, fastest, or most intelligent animals for survival.
And from most indications, we humans are among the
most intelligent, the most adaptable of all living beings.
So if the apes cannot make their way in this rapidly changing world, why shouldn't they join the dinosaurs, Proconsul, and the thousands of other species which have slipped
over the edge into oblivion? The answer is not simple.

First, there is a selfish answer: we need them. The
primates, because they resemble man so closely, have taught
us much about ourselves. They have been used in medicine
to learn more about physical and mental diseases. One
human ailment, polio, has been conquered thanks to a
serum developed by using monkeys. In another area of science, the apes helped in our space effort, for they were
America's first travellers into that vacuum that exists above
the atmosphere. From their trips, we learned how the human body would react to weightlessness, how well it could
perform tasks, and what would happen to it when it
plunged back into the atmosphere. The study of free-living
primates has given us many clues to man's behavior—how
and why he relates with his fellow man as he does. And as

scientific studies of apes continue, we shall undoubtedly learn still more that is important to our well-being. If we allow them to disappear, this valuable source of information will be cut off.

There is another area of science—ecology—where the apes might be of value to us if we let them live. Ecology is the study of the way that living things relate to each other and to their environment. Earlier, we used the term "ecological niche," which we described as that environment in which an animal fits. It has to do with food, temperature, the degree of wetness or dryness in the environment, and so forth. Ecology, or the ecological niche, also refers to how an animal relates to the animals around it. For instance, there is a little bird in Africa called the honey guide. This bird, because of the way its digestive system is designed, thrives on beeswax. But before it can get at the wax, the bees' nest must be opened, and the honey guide isn't capable of doing this. So it gets help. It attracts the attention of another animal, a honey badger or a baboon or a native, and leads him to the nest. After the helper has opened the nest and taken the honey, the bird eats the wax. The honey guide has a direct ecological relationship with the animal who opens the bees' nest, a relationship that is good for both creatures.

Each ecological niche is part of what is called an ecological community. Here is one simple example of such a community: Earthworms dig through the ground; they keep it loose for water to seep down, and enrich it with their dead bodies. They help the grass to grow, which produces better cattle. These cattle provide finer beef for humans, who in turn grow stronger and stay healthier.

So we can say that humans are a part of the ecological community that includes cattle, grass, and earthworms.

There are millions of such relationships, and because man is a being who shares the earth with all other living things, he is joined in some sort of relationship to each of them. We have come to this realization only recently. For much of our history, we assumed that we were separate from other life, that we were special and could do whatever we wanted to nature. Now, at last, we are beginning to see how false this is.

But we are only beginning, and there are vast areas where we know little or nothing. Until we learn far more, we must not disturb the world's ecological communities any more than is necessary, for, once upset, they seldom if ever return to their original condition. Here is another example, showing how man, through ignorance, can ultimately harm himself. About twenty years ago, we began using a powerful new pesticide, DDT, to kill harmful insects. We started to use it without first studying its long-term effects. DDT does a thorough job, so thorough, in fact, that it doesn't know when to stop. It stays in the ground, and slowly washes into the streams. Fish eat it and the poison accumulates in their livers. Men and wildlife eat the fish and slowly the DDT builds up within their bodies. This poison is used so widely that some authorities state that there is no place on earth that is free of DDT. And we still do not know what will be the final result of our thoughtless use of it. Currently, there is evidence that it destroys the body's ability to store vitamin A.

We really do not know how all of life's many forms fit together in the magnificent design which has evolved over the past two billion years. It might be very much to our benefit as a species to save as much of the natural world, including the apes, for that time when we do know.

There are other reasons to save the apes from extinction. One of them, and one which more and more people are accepting, has nothing to do with science or man's physical welfare. It is a moral reason.

Our cousins, the apes, have the right to exist simply because they do exist. After all, they, like us, are one of nature's experiments, and as such they deserve the right to live out their role, whatever it is. We humans chose to use our magnificent brain to learn many things—to use fire, to invent the wheel, to read and write, raise skyscrapers, explore outer space. Perhaps now is the time for our brain to learn humility, a reverence for life. We might discover that simply because we chose to walk away from the forest a couple of million years ago, we do not have the right to destroy those who, for whatever reason, stayed behind.

IN APPRECIATION

DURING THE PAST FEW YEARS, many dedicated people have left the comfort and safety of civilization in order to better study the great apes. They have travelled to Africa and Asia to live in the most primitive of conditions while they observed chimpanzees, gorillas, orangutans, and gibbons. What they have learned has given us invaluable information about our closest living relatives. Most of the material in this book is based on their findings. However, the book's *contents* are my responsibility only.

There are too many of these dedicated scientists, naturalists, and conservationists to be named here. I hope that by remembering the few listed below, I can say "Thank you" to the many.

They are: Irven DeVore, ape and monkey behavior; Clarence R. Carpenter, gibbons and howler monkeys; Jane Goodall, chimpanzees; Mr. and Mrs. Tom Harrison, orangutans; Louis Leakey, anthropology; Desmond and Ramona Morris, anthropoid apes; Vernon Reynolds, chimpanzees; George Schaller, gorillas; E. L. Simons and D. E. Pilbeam, primate evolution.

FURTHER READING

Perhaps you will enjoy reading more about our cousins the apes. Here are a few of the many fine books which will interest you.

Eimerl, Sarel and DeVore, Irven, *The Primates*. New York: Time Inc., 1965.

Harrison, Barbara, *Orang-Utan*. London: Collins, 1962.

Morris, Desmond and Ramona, *Men and Apes*. New York: McGraw-Hill Book Company, 1966.

Reynolds, Vernon, *The Apes*. New York: E. P. Dutton & Co., Inc., 1967.

Reynolds, Vernon, *Budongo*. Garden City, N. Y.: The Natural History Press, 1965.

Schaller, George, *The Year of the Gorilla*. Chicago: University of Chicago Press, 1964.

Van Lawick-Goodall, Baroness Jane, *My Friends the Wild Chimpanzees*. Washington, D.C.: National Geographic Society, 1967.

INDEX

Figures in italics indicate illustrations